Something in the Way
AN ALZHEIMER'S CHRONICLE

Something in the Way

AN ALZHEIMER'S CHRONICLE

Bebe Bralley

Preface by Gary T. Garner
Afterword by Loralu Raburn, M.D.

Bebe Bralley is a real-estate broker with her own company, TexStar Realty, in Ingleside, Texas.

Gary T. Garner of Amarillo is a retired professor of music at West Texas A&M University.

Dr. Loralu Raburn of Amarillo is the founder and owner of Clarity Endeavors, a company devoted to educating the public about brain diseases.

ROSEPEN

RosePen Books, Dallas, Texas 75254
©2014 by Bryan A. Garner
All rights reserved. Published 2014.
Printed in the United States of America.

ISBN-13: 978-0-9796060-6-9

Contents

Preface

GARY T. GARNER

I'm not quite sure just how Bill Bralley and I became such great friends. We first met as high-school sophomores and somehow he, Jack Fuqua, Jim Sharp, Joe Wells, and I quickly became a tight-knit group of five. We dubbed ourselves the "Inner Circle," a designation in which we took no little pride.

After three years of incredible camaraderie and what in retrospect seems like nonstop fun and riotous laughter, high school ended, and we all went off to college. Bralley (pronounced BRAH-lee)—none of us ever called him by his first name—and I went to Texas Tech, where we roomed together for a couple of years before the Korean War and Uncle Sam intervened, at least for me. Bralley was blind in one eye, owing to a tragic childhood accident, rendering him ineligible for military service.

Before leaving for Tech, we pooled our resources to buy a 1932 Chevy convertible, a vehicle I'm certain we pushed far more than we ever drove. For the most part, his beloved red Indian motorcycle was our chief means of transportation. At some point, however, he managed to put together enough money to purchase a 1941 Ford convertible, and our transportation fortunes improved dramatically.

I was in the Air Force in 1951 when I got married, and of course Bralley was my best man. I'll never forget walking to the altar with him just behind me, repeatedly whispering, audible only to me, "Bye-bye, G.G."

By now our lives were going in decidedly different directions and we were largely out of touch for some time. Then one day in 1953 our telephone rang, and it was Bralley, telling me that I was to be in Silverton a few days later for his wedding, and that I was to be at the rehearsal.

Silverton is a small Texas town about 88 miles from Lubbock, where we were living; my wife Mariellen and I duly reported to the church at the specified time. We were seated a few pews behind Bralley as we awaited the arrival of the minister. He turned to me and said, very casually, "G.G., you want to be the best man?"

"Uh, sure, if you want me to, but you don't need to feel under any obligation."

"Nah, go on and do it." So I did. That's a pretty good little snapshot of Bill Bralley. A meticulous planner he was not. "Shoot from the hip" is the phrase that most readily comes to mind. It was part of his great charm.

But the real importance of this event has to do with what I later came to realize was the best decision he ever made: marrying Bebe. She's a woman unlike any I've ever known. It would be impossible to find the words to describe her adequately. If I were forced to try, I suppose I'd start with such adjectives as tough, indefatigable, upbeat, positive, loyal—the list could go on endlessly but still not come even remotely close to doing her justice.

Here's an example of just how tough this amazing lady is. Bralley and Bebe spent several years on their beautiful ranch near Groom, Texas. Mariellen and I were still in Lubbock when I received a call from Bralley telling me there was to be an Inner Circle reunion that weekend, and of course my attendance was mandatory. I had other plans, but I canceled them and made the 160-mile trip to the ranch. When I got there, I saw that Bebe was out branding cattle. Pretty impressive, I thought, but it was only later that I learned it was more impressive than I'd realized: she'd had a miscarriage just the day before! Only Bebe.

All these qualities—the toughness; the optimism; the loving, caring compassion—all come through in this gripping day-by-day chronicle that Bebe so carefully kept during Bralley's long illness. It's a wonderful, sometimes funny, sometimes searing, always uplifting account of the trials she lived through that will be both instructive and inspirational to other caregivers. As much as anything, though, it's a love story, one I dare say will bring tears to the eyes of anyone who reads it. It's pretty much stream-of-consciousness, written in Bebe's own inimitable voice, with only limited editing, all of which only adds to its charm and immediacy.

By the time Bralley was diagnosed, the Inner Circle was already down by one: Joe had left us three or four years earlier. When Bralley's sad news reached the remaining three of us, we made immediate plans to fly to Corpus Christi, where we rented a car and drove to their home in Portland, Texas, in effect to say goodbye.

Despite the inevitability we knew lay ahead, it was a positively glorious weekend. Bralley's memory of the "old days" was still seemingly intact, and we revisited them with gusto.

And Bebe. She just couldn't do enough for us, and her infectious laughter and cheery demeanor turned what might well have been something like a wake into a celebration—a celebration of a life and a friendship that meant, and will always mean, so very much to all of us. The life of an exceptional man.

When Bebe and I had a long phone conversation not long ago, she told me about several of her widowed friends who've remarried. She jokingly remarked that it brought to mind a popular song from many years ago—"Wedding Bells Are Breaking Up That Old Gang of Mine." When someone asked if she were ever likely to remarry, her emphatic reply was, "No. How *could* I when I've already had the best?" Indeed she had. And so had Bralley.

The Inner Circle's down to two now. We lost Sharp a couple of years ago. One of my most cherished possessions is a picture I keep under the glass on my desk, a photograph of Bralley and Sharp laughing lustily during that last visit. And how, it might be asked, do I happen to have that picture? Why, Bebe sent it. Of course. Bebe.

Introduction

BEBE BRALLEY

Bill Bralley and I married in Silverton, Texas, in the Methodist Church on Saturday, August 8, 1953. We lived our young married lives on a ranch 55 miles east of Amarillo, Texas, 12 miles east of Groom.

We lived a very carefree life, doing all our work together as partners. In our sixth year of marriage, we had a baby daughter, Toni Lynn, who was followed 15 months later by a son, Mitchel Weatley. Another great son, William Tyler, came along about four years later. And five years after that, Vicki Suzanne completed our family.

We bought another home in Port Aransas, Texas, in 1965 because Mitch suffered from asthma, and it seemed ocean air was the only thing that helped. That was the beginning of our living in two different locations, an arrangement that continued for years.

While in Port Aransas, Bill developed a nice second-home subdivision, Seagull Isle. I served as the sales agent for the lots and homes. We all enjoyed the island life and the friends there. Simply living the carefree island life was, for us, the best of the best. We quickly adapted to deep-sea fishing, picnics on the beach, and all the pleasures a small island can offer.

When Toni reached her high-school years, it was time to go home again. There was no high school in Port Aransas, so we moved the whole family back to the ranch to attend school in Groom. We both thought this was another good move, and it proved to be great for the kids. They took to the country life, and they loved it.

We had some of the dearest friends of our lives in Groom, so we were all warmly welcomed back to the Panhandle of Texas. During this time, Bill built a KOA Kampground on I-40. While he did the outside part, I ran the office and the store. Bill also went back into the cattle business.

The children thrived. They loved the ranch and the life it offered. We remained there until deciding to move back to Amarillo in 1979. I had wanted to go into real estate since I'd grown to enjoy it in Port Aransas, but I didn't actually do much because we continued to take every chance we got to return to our island. Eventually, when our youngest, Suzanne, graduated from high school, we moved back to the Texas coast. We kept only some farmland and settled back into the slow-moving South Texas life we both loved.

Bill and I were living in Ingleside, where I was working in the mortgage-loan business, when odd things started happening. The children and I started noticing that Bill wasn't acting normally, although no one really knew what was wrong.

We all knew Bill was not himself. There were little things. He wouldn't get in a boat anymore. He didn't like leaving the house. This was clearly not normal, but I have always felt that I simply don't know what to notice or how to know when something's wrong—until it's too late.

We were a couple that had shared a very happy, successful, lucky life. I think we probably had more fun than a lot of people. We were able to enjoy each day of our shared lives from the very beginning. We always said we were best friends and considered that we had each other's backs, no matter what. There are no regrets, just a lot of wonderful memories of good times, good friends, and sharing life with four remarkable children.

The following notes are from my visits with Bill from the time the changes started becoming very noticeable until his death. I have always kept a diary, so recording these events came naturally to me. I have tried to be utterly honest and factual here, without the BS and sugarcoating that might seem so tempting. These are the facts—and just the facts. If others can learn from Bill's and my experience, that's all the reward I could ask for. I was with Bill almost every day, always thinking that something might happen that would just turn this thing around. I was with him at the moment of death. It was a sad passing and the end of an affair that never ended. But the memories will always be there.

Although our luck may have run out, the memories won't.

2007

A YEAR OF
DAWNING REALIZATION

A Golden Mind Stoops

You think you *know* the one you love, especially after 50 years. Or do you? Bill and I could finish each other's stories, order food and drinks for each other, and we always knew what the other was in the mood for—or not. Unlike a lot of couples, we have always worked together, and for us it worked. We respected each other's ideas and welcomed the other's new views on things, whether it was work or play—and we did a lot of playing too.

Bill started acting strangely earlier this year. It was the small details that made me wonder why he was doing some of the things he did. He would ask me the same questions over and over again. And he seemed to be forgetting things more and more. He did say a time or two that he "wasn't thinking right." He'd also frequently ask me about our business and whether everything was okay. I would just laugh and say yes, and he would respond with a smile or laugh and say "yeah" understandingly.

He began depending on me to carry on the conversations almost completely when visitors came. He had gotten to the point where he didn't want to go to our friends' houses at all—even to our children's homes.

When we did have visitors, Bill seemed happy. But sometimes he appeared to be completely bored with the conversation, and he'd turn away simply not to listen. Later, after our guests left, I would scold him for being rude. He didn't seem to even know what I was talking about, brushing the reprimand off.

We sold our ranch near Amarillo, Texas, a few years ago. Since then, I have worked from my home office. In the past, this had worked for us. Bill respected my working hours and gave me my space so I could finish my work on time. After my usual closing time, we would always have our dinner and evening drinks together. It was our routine. And once a month we slipped off to Mexico for a fun weekend. He'd get his hair cut there by his favorite barber.

Late in the fall of 2007 I looked out my office window and saw Bill talking to our gardener, Alfonso. Bill was throwing his hands up in the air and walking all around his pickup. Finally, Alfonso got into the truck, quickly got back out again, and smiled at Bill. They both laughed, and Bill got in and drove off. I walked out and asked Alfonso what was going on. He just smiled and told me Bill couldn't start his truck. I asked why and Alfonso said, "He was trying to start it with his pocket knife." I couldn't believe it. "What did you do?" I asked Alfonso. "I took the key he was holding in his other hand and put it in the ignition and started the pickup for him."

Many odd little things started happening. Unusual things for Bill. For example, he always helped around the house by carrying the laundry basket to the laundry room, unloading the dishwasher, carrying the trash out, and other odds and ends. Suddenly he stopped all that. When I'd asked him to bring the laundry down, he would look at me and do nothing. Sometimes he would just say, "Not now." I later learned that he would use these noncommittal answers when he didn't know what to do.

Much more started happening. On the first of December 2007, he came into my office around 10:00 a.m., still in his robe, saying, "I can't find my brush stuff." All his personal toiletries have been in the same drawer in every house we have ever lived in. I just looked up and said, "Go look on your side of the vanity, next to the shower. It's there." He came back with a big bottle of hair conditioner in his hand, very upset and getting mad. I went back to the bathroom with him and saw that all the drawers and cabinets were open, both in the bathroom and in the hall. I took him into the bathroom and showed him his toiletry drawer. Then I left him to dress. It took about two hours for him to get dressed—and his hair still wasn't brushed.

DECEMBER 12, 2007

Our son Tye brought us a baked chicken. He told us some great stories about how he was getting ready to leave on a deep-sea fishing trip for a month off the coast of Louisiana. Tye is a well-respected boat captain who manages yachts for companies that fish around the world. We always love his adventurous stories.

During Tye's stories, I noticed that Bill was very quiet. He seemed not to hear a word of the conversation and eventually turned toward the bookcases along the wall. His eyes browsed the shelves as if he were looking for something in particular. Later in the evening, I mentioned Tye and how good the chicken dinner was. Bill didn't even realize that Tye had been to see us earlier in the day. I said, "You remember he was here this morning." Bill just looked at me, nodded his head, and whispered, "Oh, yeah."

DECEMBER 29, 2007

Bill came home very frustrated. He had just come back from the Stripes gas station, where we have bought gas for years. He was cussing and vowing that we'd never go back there again. After some fishing through the conversation, I finally gathered that he had not been able to use his credit card at the gas station—he had no idea how to use it.

It's a slow realization that things are changing with my Bill: he'll ask me about the name of the town we live in, he gets confused about the different rooms in the house, he's irritated when I ask him to go to the bedroom or bathroom, and he's even started to lock every door in the house—even the bathroom door when he walks out. I've had to get the little builder's key to unlock everything.

He's been misplacing *everything*.

And now he can't use the TV controls anymore. He's tried to change the television stations with his electric razor and even his keys. And he gets mad at the TV all the time. He can't think of the names of ordinary objects. And he's reading only the sports page of the newspaper now, and *always* takes at least two hours to get dressed. He simply does not know whether he has taken his medicine or not—and doesn't seem to care. He has become obsessed with the cat and dog.

DECEMBER 31, 2007

Having always showered and shaved daily, Bill has absolutely quit showering. We are constantly fighting about this now. It's been over a week. I had to throw a fit to make him get in the shower, then had to show him how to use the soap and how to shampoo his hair. His head is getting little scabs on it from not being shampooed enough, so I am getting some new shampoo that is supposed to help this problem. (Now if I can only get it on his head.)

He is putting the same clothes on daily. I have to grab them and run to the washer before he puts them on again. Then sometimes he will just sit there until I select the clothes to put on. He gets mad a lot and calls me all the time, and then he gets madder if I am not there in an instant. Right now it's 10 o'clock and he is just now starting to get dressed.

Bathing has become a continual problem, and he is "lost" almost all the time. He just has so much trouble with the rooms. Today he wanted to call his friend, Bubba Patton, one of his high-school friends who became a doctor and later delivered our first son, Mitch, in 1960. But Bubba was killed in 1962. Bill didn't believe me when I said Bubba was dead.

2008

A MEMORABLE YEAR OF
ONCOMING OBLIVION

Lost & Found

Bill's habit had long been to get the mail daily. He left to go to the Post Office, which is about seven blocks from our house. Finally, he came home in a panic. He said, "Bebe, I have been lost—really lost!" I laughed and then he did too. Then, very seriously, Bill said: "Bebe, I was really lost, I didn't think I would ever get home again." That hit me. I knew at that moment that something was really wrong, but I didn't think it was anything we couldn't handle and work on together.

That afternoon, I drove us to Mac's Barbecue, where we have gone at least once a month for ten years. He wanted to know where we were. Then he started waving at people— everybody. He didn't know them. Bill is a very quiet man. He's never even waved at someone on the road, but he today waved at everyone as if they were best friends. His concentration is very short. He flies off the handle easily over nothing.

FEBRUARY 22, 2008

Today Bill cannot tell the fridge from the upright freezer, and he doesn't know how to get ice from the icemaker. He simply cannot tell one room from the other.

FEBRUARY 29, 2008

Today, for the first time, Bill absolutely panicked when he couldn't find me. I had run to the post office to get some stamps. I had told him where I was going and that I'd be right back. He was seriously frightened. When I got back he just held and held me and said, "Don't leave me again!" He wouldn't go with me because he can't leave the cat and dog. He thinks someone will steal them. Believe me, they wouldn't.

APRIL 1, 2008

I can't find any brushes. The TV control is gone. The keys are gone. And now all my brushes are gone. This is the first time Bill has gotten in my vanity drawers. He can't find the bathroom, and the problem is that it's often too late by the time he lets me know he needs to go to the bathroom. He has lost his billfold. He doesn't want to take any medicine. He asks the same things over and over and over. He doesn't know our address or phone number. He is wearing the same clothes every day, and of course they are really dirty. I am having to grab them at bedtime, although sometimes he doesn't take them all off. Still locking all the doors. I have wised up and keep my keys on me all the time and another set for everything hidden outside.

Although he never wants to leave the house, the other day he said, "I think we should move back to the ranch." (We sold the ranch in 1984.) He is getting irritated more and more. Bill has quit reading the newspaper altogether. Sometimes he looks at the fishing pictures in the Port Aransas paper. He doesn't seem to care for TV anymore, though he has always loved TV and movies. Sometimes he will watch the old Westerns. He doesn't like the new shows, and when I say, "Hey, this looks like a good one. Let's watch it," he will say, "Oh, we saw that show last year." And then he'll get up and walk away. Sometimes he will eat something and say, "I remember when you used to make this." I had just made it.

This evening he went to make me a Scotch and water. I have been drinking Scotch and water for 30 years—the exact same way every evening—and he always fixes it. He couldn't find any ice, so I showed him the icemaker again, finally got the ice into the glass—then he didn't know what to do and brought me a glass of ice water. He gets frustrated when I tell him what he has done. He doesn't seem to remember anything I tell him. I have found it's better to laugh about things and do them myself.

APRIL 7, 2008

Bill had been sitting in his pickup a long time and finally came in mad as could be. He said nothing works. We have to get a new pickup. I went out there and sure enough, nothing worked. Finally, the yardman came and said the battery was run down because everything was turned on and had probably been on for a long time. He hooked up the battery charger, which Bill didn't know how to do, although he has done it hundreds of times at the ranch. It wouldn't charge up, so we called the mechanic, and he said we had to have a new battery. Bill got really mad at the mechanic. But we got the new battery.

APRIL 8, 2008

Bill won't take his medicine. He thinks he is supposed to take Alka-Seltzer all the time. I have to force his blood pressure and cholesterol pills down him. After I told the doctor, he talked to Bill—just normal and all—which meant absolutely nothing to him. Tonight he didn't even know we had been to the doctor.

APRIL 30, 2008

Concentration completely gone, Bill can't follow the most simple directions. Asked to get his billfold off the nightstand, he will go look in the kitchen. Now he puts everything "up"— on top of the chest of drawers. Then he will look and look for it. I am getting pretty good at finding the hiding places now. Sometimes he walks around with his hands full of combs and brushes—then hides them all. Sometimes I have a real hunt on my hands. If a crazy show comes on—cartoons, or a Spanish-language show—he will just sit there like he is enjoying it until I come in and change it. He never complains. He just sits.

He's still locking all the doors, and if I ring the doorbell to get in after I'm locked out, he won't answer the door. I make sure have to have my keys all the time. But I've forgotten when just stepping out the door for a second—and sure enough, tick-a-lock, I'm out.

I've found that I can get Bill to ride with me sometimes if we take the dog. Work takes me to downtown Corpus today, so now I load up the dog and Bill.

Knowing Home

I was so excited. Bill agreed to go to Mexico and stay in "our" little motel in Weslaco, Texas, where his favorite barber is. This was really exciting for me: to get away like we used to. He always loved this, and it has been over three months since we have been there. So it was a big deal to me to "get away." Bill complained all the way down that his stomach hurt and that he wanted to go back home, but he ate well on the way and seemed to be okay. I thought he just wanted to go back to the dog. We got there about four o'clock. After unpacking, I went to a little Italian restaurant to get some food to bring back to the room for us. I brought back a nice dinner and set it on the little table by the window overlooking the pool, and thought, This is so peaceful and relaxing. Wow, this is just great. I poured us some wine to go with the parmesan chicken and said, "Come on, let's eat." I sat down and he just kept standing and looking really strange. Finally, he came over and sat down and changed personalities. He was really nice. He is always that way when he doesn't really know someone or has just met them. He very politely took a few bites and looked over at me and said, "Bebe used to make some stuff like this." I kind of laughed and then he said something else that Bebe did a long time ago. I kind of laughed again, and we ate and watched the TV. Then out of the blue he said, "I want to go home." I said, "Well, we will in the morning," and I started getting ready for bed. Bill looked at me funny and would not come to bed or get undressed. Finally, I persuaded him to lie down on the bed—fully dressed. He lay down far on the other side from me. I gave him a sleeping pill with his other medicines, thinking that would get him down and asleep. He was up again at 1:00 a.m. looking for "his" dog, very disoriented, needing to go to the bathroom but couldn't find it. I kept showing him the bathroom, but he would not pay any attention to me. I could tell I was really irritating him. After finally getting him in the bathroom he said very loudly "I want Bebe right now. She will be looking for me!" He was still being polite but plainly fed up with me. He did not know me at all. That was the first time that had happened, and it was a terrible, strange feeling that I didn't like. I knew something was way more wrong than I had previously thought.

There was no more waiting around. He was pacing and ready to bolt out the door. I grabbed a big strong cup of motel coffee and said, "Bill, I am loading the car and we will leave right now." It was around five in the morning, and I was absolutely beat. After getting us loaded while Bill just stood there watching, I got him in the car and we headed home to the coast. As soon as we were on the road, he started asking, "How long will it take to get to Amarillo?" I just said, "A while." He was very quiet, not talking at all but staring out the window.

Then all of a sudden he looked so happy. He said "Oh, I know where we are now: that's Boy's Ranch right over there, so I know we are close to Amarillo. We are on that road from Dalhart to Amarillo." He kept thinking we were northwest of Amarillo, where he lived his life before going away for college. Of course, we were down by the Mexican border—nowhere near Amarillo. He started asking about going to the ranch. Finally, I told him that we had sold the ranch 25 years ago. He was shocked. He wanted to know who bought it, and where we live now. At least he seemed to be knowing me again, and that felt better. My hopes were up. His legs started shaking badly. They had also been shaking during the night. But this time it was worse. He said he was feeling very weak. He had mentioned feeling weak during the night too. In fact, one time he had sat down when we were putting a clean shirt on him and had said, "I can't think a thing at all. What's happening to me?" I gave him a Valium—that was all I had at the time— just to get him into the car.

Bill was totally exhausted when we got home (it is a two-and-a-half-hour drive). So was I. But when we got home, instead of resting or lying down, he started walking and walking and walking. He would not sit down or anything. He just kept walking and asking where the bathroom was. By now it was only noon, but it had already been a long day.

MAY 4, 2008

Bill slept late and woke up completely disoriented, not knowing where he was. Although his stomach hurt, he ate a good breakfast and walked all day long. I mean *all* day. He couldn't concentrate on anything—driving me crazy. I am so tired.

Bill seems to be getting worse each day, and he's acting so strange. All he wants to know is when are we "going home." He thinks our house is a motel and keeps all the doors closed—to keep the other people out. He will not step out of our bedroom unless he is completely dressed (even though he's in the same dirty clothes). He doesn't want "the people" to see him in his underwear. I finally got him bathed on Sunday after standing in the shower with him, and I trimmed his hair. It was so long it was on his shoulders and simply had to be cut. It is so hard to keep, and it's usually dirty (he has beautiful thick curly hair). He does not even try to brush his hair or teeth anymore.

I have noticed that he doesn't get words right, and he seems to think a long time before speaking. When the A/C is too cool, he says, "I'm cold, turn off the refrigerator." He has now lost three more sets of pickup keys. I had five sets made this time. He has started saying that he is leaving for the ranch the first thing in the morning. I found the razor stuffed down in the socks—in the very back of sock drawer—and a complete ice-cream stick in the pantry. Thank God it was still in the paper. He's still scared to death that someone will steal the dog, Sugar.

Today I said, "Will you carry the laundry basket to the laundry room?" I pointed to the basket. He picked it up and took it straight to the living room. I said, "No, the laundry room." He got mad and said, "I don't know where the damn laundry room is or what laundry room means," then just walked off.

He doesn't try to read the newspaper, but he does try to change TV channels with the razor or keys. And he's started wetting his pants. I will say, "Go change your pants." He takes them and hangs them on the vines on the back patio. Then I steal them and wash them. He doesn't realize he needs to go and sometimes I don't think he knows he has peed until it is over. Then he doesn't want me to know.

He doesn't drive anymore, but he goes out and cusses the pickup every day. He walks all around it. He is getting more agitated all the time. I have noticed that he gets more restless and nervous starting around 2:00 in the afternoon. It just goes downhill from there. Most days he walks until bedtime.

JULY 1, 2008

Everything is still about the same, only now Bill is getting distorted memories. He thinks his mother had a lot of miscarriages. (She was never pregnant—Bill was adopted.) I was the one who had several miscarriages. He keeps asking me over and over: "When we are going home?" He doesn't know one room from another. I will say, "Bill, go to your chair in the living room and I will bring you a sandwich." He looks at me like I am crazy and says, "Where the hell is the living room?"

His hair is just so long. All I can do is try to spray and brush it a little. He won't go to a barber at all. He took all his underwear out of the drawer and crammed everything into his Levi drawer and was trying to shove it shut when I walked in. He was very frustrated because it wouldn't close. He is afraid someone will steal his pickup—so he is continually watching it. He walks around it all the time.

He has started depending on me for everything, yet he can act so normal when guests drop by. He doesn't actually enter the conversation but will make the appropriate smiles and laughs with everyone. He will hug me and say, "Oh Bebe, I don't know what I would do without you. Please promise you will always be here. Something is wrong and I don't know what." This is what is so sad. He knows something is very wrong. This just breaks my heart. It is so sad.

JULY 15, 2008

Well, this just beats all. Now he is wrapping things up in handkerchiefs or washrags and hiding them in places, mostly his chest of drawers and closet. But he puts them way behind other things, or in his boots. He is hiding things he wants to use, like his gold pen and pencil, which he has carried for 40 years in his shirt pocket. I found his razor all wrapped up inside some Levis—after we had looked for two days.

He can't follow instructions of any kind, like "Go brush your teeth." Even when I led him to the bathroom, he will just stand there and look at me. Then he'll start walking, walking, walking—looks as if it would wear him down, but it doesn't.

JULY 15, 2008

He gets mad because all the doors are locked and he simply can't figure it out. But of course, he is the one locking the doors. I really have to depend on *my* hiding places for extra keys. I have even had to use those tiny little screwdrivers sometimes. He makes me get more inventive, even though I'm not inclined that way. But you know, you learn things when you have to.

JULY 30, 2008

Toward the end of July, when our older daughter, Toni, and her husband, Jeff, came for a few days to visit, he acted more normal than usual. I did notice that he depends on me more and more to finish sentences and carry the conversation. He really enjoyed sitting on the porch and visiting with them. Toni mentioned that she thought Daddy was doing a lot better than when she was here in January. I didn't comment.

The following week, his dearest friends from first grade on came down for a visit from Amarillo. Jackie Fuqua and Jim Sharp were friends that he started first grade with, and Gary Garner was his high-school buddy and college roommate—and best man in our wedding. He was so excited and really ready for a good visit. Bill had quit going out to eat a while ago—in fact does not like to leave the house, just wants to stay right here—so it worked well with all the guys sitting on the porch remembering the good old times as I prepared food to eat here at home. We didn't have to go out, even though they invited us out for dinners. I always gave excuses.

He recognized Jackie and Gary, but he never knew Jim and kept asking me, "Who is the big guy?" I would tell him and tell him, but he never did really know. Bill would act like he remembered every story. I took lots of pictures and showed him afterwards. Every time he looked at them, it was as if he was seeing them for the first time. He thoroughly enjoyed the visit, and he really seemed more normal than he has in a long, long, long time. I don't think they will ever see him again. If they do, Bill will most certainly not know it. July was a better month than most. Maybe things will get better.

AUGUST 1, 2008

We ate dinner in the living room, as we usually do, and I carried my plate into the kitchen. Bill said, "What do you want me to do with mine?" I said, "Well, just carry it in the kitchen." When we went to bed, there was the plate in the master bathroom. All day he has been wanting to know how we are going to get both cars to the Panhandle. Will he follow me or will I follow him? When are we leaving? Then he said, "I want to go tomorrow. I don't want to come back to this motel. I don't like the people here, and I don't like this motel." He wants to go home tomorrow.

AUGUST 6, 2008

As soon as we got up he said, "When are we leaving, and how will we get both cars there? You know I have to have my pickup to work." Then he laughed and said, "I tell you one thing. I am kissing this place goodbye." Sometimes I get tickled at his expressions. They are so "him."

Backward Mind

Can't believe it. He's lost all the keys again. I had left some out, and swish! Away they went. I went downtown and had five more sets made, but not the post-office key. It's too expensive, and he doesn't go anymore.

Today Bill came up to me and said, "Bebe, something is wrong with me." Very factual. These little things let me know that he does realize something is really wrong. He lost the ability to concentrate a long time ago, but it seems he has taken a real turn downhill.

I got him in the shower—after 14 days of trying. (Whee!) He has been wearing almost the same clothes all this time. He sleeps in them a lot. His stomach hurts nearly all the time now. We went to our family doctor, and he gave him some more medicine and put him on a new Alzheimer's medication called Aricept.

He still has lost all judgment: he will eat some of his food and put the plate on the floor for the dog to eat, then pick it up and eat some more or just walk off. I have told him over and over not to do that. It nearly makes me sick, but still he does it.

SEPTEMBER 14, 2008

He didn't get dressed all day today, and his stomach hurt badly. At three o'clock this afternoon he sat in his chair with Sugar and asked me whether that's our dog. I said yes. He asked how long we've had this dog. Then: "I think it is a good dog."

SEPTEMBER 16, 2008

Bill can't tell the freezer from the fridge and gets mad because he will go to the freezer and say, "We don't have any milk or anything to eat." He unplugged my bedside clock and put it in his house slippers in the back of his closet. Then he put a whole box of shotgun shells in the other shoe. I saw him trying to cram some more stuff into the slippers. That's when I caught on.

I usually bring us taquitos to eat after church, and today I had to show him how to eat one. He simply could not figure out what to do with it and kept trying to unwrap it. I would rewrap it and say, "Just hold it like this and eat."

SEPTEMBER 21, 2008

Really confused today, Bill took a shower while I was at church and was sitting naked when I got home because he couldn't find any clothes. I got him dressed, and we went to the little store to get some ice. I thought I would send him in for the ice to see how he did. Pretty simple—right? He went in and came right back out laughing said, "What did you want?" I told him ice. So he went back and finally came back out with ice. I was happy, thinking he'd done it. Just as he was getting in the car, the boy came running out and said he'd left his billfold on the counter after giving him $50 for the ice without waiting for change. I went in and got the change and the billfold, and thanked the boy.

Our son Tye brought us a lot of good dove (which we love), but it still needed cleaning. After Tye left, Bill didn't know what to do. He has been hunting and cleaning dove since he was 13 years old. Everything seems to have gone backwards today. And he insists that he wants to go home.

SEPTEMBER 25, 2008

Our family doctor suggested that I get long-term-care insurance, so I made an appointment with an agent who was coming by today. I had gone over everything I could think of with Bill and told him to be sure and answer all her questions. I wasn't allowed to stay in there with him while she interviewed him, but I cracked the office door so I could hear. She asked a lot of questions and was so nice. I could tell she was trying to help him on some answers, but he got completely confused and very frustrated. Finally, she asked for his address again, and he said, "1911 Van Buren, Amarillo, Texas." (He lived there as a small boy.) I guess that really blew it. After she left, he said: "That was the most boring ole gal I ever saw. She didn't know what she was doing at all. I don't know what the hell she wanted—do you?'

SEPTEMBER 27, 2008

Another one of Bill's dearest friends, Scotty Witt, came from Amarillo today. Bill loves Scotty dearly, and they've been hunting-and-fishing buddies since childhood. Scotty stayed about four hours and we had a most enjoyable visit. I did notice that Bill had gone into his very polite mode, but I still thought he knew Scotty because he laughed at the right things and acted pretty normal—except for being so polite. As Scotty was leaving we walked out with him and while standing on the sidewalk Bill asked Scotty whether he knew Deon Witt. Scotty laughed and said, "Well, yes Bill, you know that's my little brother." Bill looked kind of funny and said, "Well, do you know Scotty Witt?" Scotty just reached over and hugged Bill and said, "Bill, I am Scotty Witt." He told Bill he loved him and left. Bill looked so sad, he looked at me and said "Oh, I wish I had known that was Scotty. There is so much I wanted to talk to him about. I have wanted to see him for such a long time."

Things have gotten continually worse. Our daughter Suzanne, who lives nearby, has started coming over almost every day to help out. Bill cannot be left alone because he will just walk off with or without clothes on. The doctor has suggested that we get help to come in daily, but I don't feel I can afford that and Suzanne is a great help. We found him a block from our house, walking in stickers and thinking he was going to Harrison Street in Amarillo—some 650 miles away—to see his grandmother. I am very worried that he will hurt himself. He just doesn't understand anything.

OCTOBER 17, 2008

This morning Bill was completely disoriented and didn't know where he was at all. He is seeing people in our yard all the time who aren't there. He keeps thinking our friend H.K. Stanfield (another one of his friends from first grade) is looking in our windows and can't figure out why he's doing that. He now thinks we are in Amarillo, and he is always looking for the Amarillo streets.

At 2:20 this morning, he flipped on the bedside light and was glaring down at me. It was the meanest, craziest face I have ever seen—completely contorted. He jerked the covers off me and said "I'm going to beat you to little pieces and break your neck. I am going to kill you now!" I started crying and saying, "No, no, Bill, please don't!" But he started beating me on the head as I was pulling the covers up. I had started crying, and he said, "Make one more sound and I am breaking your neck now!" He was pounding my face and head, and I really thought I would be killed. Our little Sugar started barking and jumping up on Bill. He stopped. He looked at Sugar, turned, and walked to the bathroom. I jumped out of bed, grabbed my robe, and ran for the back through my office, grabbing my purse full of keys and my phone. I got in my car and peeled out as fast as that car would go. All I could do was cry and wonder what the hell happened. I didn't know what to do, so I drove to the beach and parked and cried and tried to figure out what is happening. I was thinking how Bill looked at me—he was completely deranged. I could not comprehend what had happened.

Around 4 o'clock in the morning, my cell phone rang. I couldn't imagine who it could be, since Bill didn't know how to use a phone and I had called no one. It was the Ingleside police. They said, "We have a man in custody saying that he is Bill Bralley and lives at 1911 Van Buren, Amarillo, Texas. But he has a card with your name on it in his pocket, and he says you're his wife." They said he was covered with blood, and did I want them to take him to the hospital, lock him up, or what? They said the wounds and bleeding did not seem to be serious. I said, "Take him home, I will be there in about 20 minutes. Stay with him, and stay with me when I get there."

I walked into our house barefoot, with stringy hair and a tear-stained face, and when Bill saw me, he ran to me wearing just his underwear and the dirty shirt he had gone to bed in. He grabbed me and hugged and hugged me and wouldn't turn loose, saying "Bebe, where have you been? I have looked and looked for you." I could tell he was all right, just dirty, bloody, and utterly confused. I told the policemen to go on. We would be all right.

We both got in the shower and I washed him and got him dressed. He was totally exhausted. I thought, Well, now I know how Joe Louis probably felt after a big fight. My face was beginning to swell, and I had a terrible headache. My face was black and blue, and so were my upper arms. I was seeing badly out of one eye, my head was throbbing, but I knew that Bill had to be taken care of immediately. I got him to bed and called the doctor as soon as I knew the office would be open, and together we decided we'd check him into the psychiatric ward on Monday. Meanwhile he gave me a prescription for Valium (I presumed for Bill). I called Suzanne, and she and her husband came over to stay with me until Monday.

I never felt safe all weekend, even though I had given him plenty of Valium. I couldn't sleep, my swollen face hurting and turning blacker. One eye was seeing little black floaters. All weekend long, he kept saying, "Bebe, those policemen may come after us because they think we have committed fraud, and we are going to have to prove we are innocent. They told me they are going to send us to the pen." He will not let me out of his sight and wants to call his mother all the time. He keeps seeing all these people outside the house, and when he's in the room with our daughter and son-in-law, he becomes very polite. He does not know them. This has been a scary, nerve-racking weekend with him begging to go home and me feeling like hell.

On Saturday afternoon, I thought maybe a little ride would do him good, so I talked him into getting into the car and going for a ride. While in the car he looked at my face and said, "What in the hell happened to your eyes and face?" (By then my eyes were nearly swollen closed.) I told him what had happened, and he said, "Oh no, oh no." He cried and hugged and hugged me, and said, "Bebe, I am so sorry. I never want to hurt you. Please forgive me. I promise to never do it again. But why didn't you get your pistol and shoot me?" I laughed and said I would have, but I couldn't reach it. He said, "Well, now, please don't shoot me or leave me. I can't live without you."

Wrapped in Dismal Thinkings

The orders came from our doctor on Monday morning. Suzanne went and made all the arrangements with the doctors, then came and picked up Bill, and I had him all clean and ready to go. He thought we were going to the doctor for his stomachaches. I did tell him the doctor would give him something to help his stomach and help him remember better. He said, "Oh good!"

When we got there, they put us in the ER. We waited waited and waited. Finally, they started blood tests and all that stuff. He hadn't eaten since early morning—a piece of toast—and he was getting really agitated around 2:00 p.m. Then they came back for more tests and to collect a urine sample. He simply could not pee for the man. They couldn't do any more until they had urine. I looked at Bill and said, "Come on, Bill. We're going to the bathroom." I turned the water on and held the cup, and he peed.

Toni, our other daughter, got in from California at 6:15 p.m.—right on time. She rented a car and came right to the hospital. We were sure glad to see her. Suzanne and I were both really worn down. The doctor came in and asked him a lot of questions. Who's president? What year is it? What month is it? Bill would just say, "I don't really care" or "It doesn't matter." But when they asked him his full name and address, he said, "William Andrew Bralley, 1911 Van Buren, Amarillo, Texas." I felt so sorry for him. He was worn out and didn't know a thing that was going on. I just wanted to answer for him so badly, as if that would make everything all right. Finally they said, "Well, we're moving him to the psychiatric ward." So Toni and I told Suzanne to go on home to her husband and little boys. It is so wonderful to have our daughters with me. Such strength they give me. I'm not sure Bill knew Toni at first because they had just given him a big shot of something, but he sure looked like he did for a while. Finally, he went to sleep just like a little boy—dead tired in the little bed in his room. I couldn't keep from crying. I felt so sorry for him, and maybe for me too. If he can get some rest and they can help him, maybe things will work out for us.

I'm still wondering what has happened. I know our world has come tumbling down, and I already miss him. It has been a long time since he has been the old Bill, but at least he was there. Even though he still thinks he is in Amarillo, and is always going to the ranch, and can't talk about daily things, I can take the wandering mind if he can just come home. But I cannot go through another night like last Friday. I have seen him get mad and double up his fist in the last two months like he wanted to hit something, but not me. It wouldn't take much to take me out. Toni is going to stay and help me with closet cleaning and trying to find lost items. What a great help to have her here. There is a lot to do, and Suzanne will come over and help arrange things. I am really going to have to work much harder on my loan business, as I already see that I am going to need more money for Bill's expenses. I definitely want to have money for whatever he needs. It is breaking my heart to see Bill like this, and I seem to cry all the time. It is a deep, deep hurt—like death. I know I will be okay and Bill will too. I just have to be very careful with money plans so Bill can have the proper help he needs.

I am already thinking of ways to cut every bill. Next week I will whittle things down some more. I have always been able to handle money pretty well and have been doing all our bills for years, so I will manage. We get to see Bill again at four o'clock tomorrow. Lord, I hope he isn't mad.

OCTOBER 21, 2008

They had a hard time with him. He wouldn't settle down. He hit the big male nurse, and they had to medicate him a lot before he finally settled down. He kept talking about the Dallas airport and his mother and different things—of course none of it making any sense.

Toni and I stayed the whole hour. He was strapped into the wheelchair, tied down completely, and he was trying to get out. One time Toni said, "Daddy, you can't get up. You have to stay there in the chair." Bill glared at her and said, "Don't go there." He isn't taking orders from anyone. No one. The nurse told us they are having a hard time trying to redirect him. I thought, Yeah, well tell me about it.

OCTOBER 22, 2008

Bill was calmer today. He talked about flying. Jabber jabber. They said on a scale of 1 to 10, yesterday was a 10, and today is a 4. So that is so much better. They've inserted a catheter and have already drained 24 ounces of urine. He's shrinking already. His stomach doesn't hurt so much and I think they will find the problem with his prostate. We'll see.

OCTOBER 24, 2008

Today he definitely knew Toni. I'm not sure he has known me during any of this, but the nurses say he asks for me all the time. But when I get there, I just don't know. Today he seemed satisfied and just talked about old friends—mostly the dead ones—and his mother. I guess she was a very loving mother, and that is good. I think childhood memories will always come back to all of us.

OCTOBER 25, 2008

I met Suzanne at the ward today, and he knew Suzanne as soon as he saw her. He was so happy to see her, but then he started talking about her as if she weren't there, and he never acknowledged me at all. He simply does not know who I am. He talked to Sugar (the dog—who wasn't there) and said to Suzanne, "Isn't she cute?" He would say, "Look at her!" Finally I said, "Where is she?" He said, "Well, right there," pointing toward the door. We just said, "Oh yeah." He said he'd been on the motorcycle all day long with Eckhart and Seewald. But he hasn't seen either of them in at least 35 years, and they are both dead. Otherwise, he was okay. We are supposed to know more on Monday, as they are running all kinds of tests each day.

OCTOBER 27, 2008

He is completely in another world. He's sleepy. He dozed off twice. But he did recognize me today and was so happy to see me. He hates the nurses because they have a catheter in him still, and he is draining a lot more urine all the time. I know this has to be helping his stomach. He seemed sad today. I know he would hate this life, if only he knew.

We'll find out more tomorrow. We'll be meeting with the counselor. Oh dear, I just wonder what can come next. We can't change yesterday and do things differently. But tomorrow may be better. I'll get by. Maybe tomorrow will give us good news and hope. Then we can plan for the future. I seem to be crying all the time. Bill is coughing a lot—a dry cough. I asked them to please check it and not let something else happen.

OCTOBER 31, 2008

Today Bill seems really sick. I was afraid of that yesterday. He is running a high fever, around 102°, and he has developed a rash from the diapers. I brought him some Depends, which are supposed to be better. They've doctored him, and they are giving him antibiotics.

By the time I arrived, they had him on a breathing machine. He is listless, but he told me he wanted us to "get going." I told him we have to get him well first. He started getting agitated, but part of that may been because he simply didn't feel good. His kidneys are not working right, so he has to stay on the catheter. They're still running tests—on everything from his brain to his kidneys. Maybe a better tomorrow.

NOVEMBER 5, 2008

I caught that terrible cough and cold that Bill has had, and I've really been down. They had him on a breathing machine and all kinds of very strong antibiotics, and then they said they were giving him the big shot, called the "voodoo shot." I wish I could have had one of those. He is using a Merry Walker, as he can't walk alone. He seems to like it. Yet he falls easily even with the Merry Walker. He's very restless, but not as agitated. And of course, he doesn't make a lick of sense. But he's settling down a little.

NOVEMBER 6, 2008

Today he could walk alone, very slowly. He still has the catheter in and sees things that aren't there. He said he talked to his mother today, and that she is better. He also said he went to class today, but that it was boring. Kind of funny, but his spirits were better and he isn't asking to leave all the time.

In fact, he said he told them to save a room for me there in the hotel. One of the nurses is named Vicki, and he thinks it is "our Vicki," our niece who lived with us a lot and seems like one of our kids. He always loved Vicki so much, so he likes that nurse.

He still trying to get over this awful cold. He seems contented but restless, and he wants to move all the time. He will not be still and whispers all the time. Most of time we can't understand him.

NOVEMBER 7, 2008

He is back in the Merry Walker because he was falling down too much. He's not making any sense of anything. He just wants to move all the time. He isn't mad or anything, just wants to move. He still has the catheter.

NOVEMBER 8, 2008

Bill was very alert today and grabbed me when I arrived. He was so happy to see me. He is walking on his own today, and he talked all the time. He was talking out loud where I could hear him. He said, "Well, let's leave for Amarillo right now." I said, "Well, we will have to wait awhile and get things ready." He said, "Well, will we take both cars or what?" Then he asked me what kind of car I had. I said the white Cadillac, and he said, "Oh yeah, like mother's car. Those are good cars; are the tires good?" I said yes, and he said, "Well, let's fill the gas tank with oil and add extra tires and go right now."

He looked better than he has in a long time. He's lost a lot of weight, his stomach is nearly flat, and he was in good spirits and wanted to know whether we had bought that place (his hospital room) or what. I said that no, we were just renting it, and he said, "Good." He never asked about home or anything. He thought he saw a little baby on his bed, but I told him it was a pillow. And he said oh, he sees little kids all the time.

I am feeling so bad I may not come tomorrow. But Suzanne will. I think I may have to stay in bed all day and go back to the doctor. Just can't shake this cold and cough. I want a voodoo shot. The counselor told me they will make a decision on Bill this coming week. Oh my, what does that mean?

NOVEMBER 10, 2008

He was better than he has been in a long time, walking by himself and kidding with the female nurses. Although he didn't make a lot of sense, he seemed happy, contented, comfortable—not irritated or restless. They said he will be leaving pretty soon, so we will see what is next. Heaven help us.

Matching Dogs with Their Names

Well, the doctor was very matter-of-fact: he said Bill cannot come home and requires professional 24-hour care. He suggested a nursing home in Rockport, Texas. We all agreed. It just made sense. They will be moving Bill to the home today.

Can you believe it? They forgot to sedate him before the move, and then forgot to pack his medications. I drove over in my car to be there, and there he was—new place, no medicine, and extremely anxious. I tried to calm him down. He thought he was on a train and that Tye was on the other train on another track. All afternoon that is all he talked about, and he got so nervous. He was afraid Tye was going to get hit by his train and he just couldn't stand that. Then he wanted to call his mother. He was really worried about her. Of course he didn't want me to leave and I didn't intend to leave until he got some meds in him. I was so tired I thought I would drop, and it was pouring down cold rain.

Finally, at 7:30 p.m. they gave him someone else's medicine and told me to go home. He was still begging me to stay when I left at 7:30, but I knew he had meds in him and would go to sleep. I will return tomorrow. Maybe things will get better. I got him a private room and bath, which I'll fix up for him. It won't be so bad until he gets to come home. Weather is terrible.

NOVEMBER 14, 2008

Bill is very confused and has stopped talking. They said he didn't sleep at all. They also said it takes a while to get settled in. He was quite agitated—in the wheelchair that he is again tied into. He is waking up around midnight, they said. That must have happened the night he attacked me. He had never woken in the middle of the night before.

NOVEMBER 15, 2008

It is a Saturday, and the weekend staff is on. Bill just mumbles and doesn't make sense. So sad. I couldn't find him when I got there, and it scared me. They didn't know where he was. Finally, when everyone was looking, we found him in someone else's room, and that person was buzzing frantically to get him out. The staff knew I was irritated with them. They said, "Well, he can't get out of the building because he has the leg bracelet on, and it buzzes if he even opens the door. He is still so confused. He has no idea where he is."

NOVEMBER 16, 2008

Bill seemed better today. But he's driving the nurses crazy. I can't help it if he won't stay in his room. When they complained to me, I feel like saying, "That's why he's here." I sure couldn't keep up with him by myself. Tye brought him a nice new big-screen TV. Maybe he'll watch that. But mostly now he just looks away and doesn't respond to anything. He's growing thin and looks bad, I think. After Mitch brought him a little fridge for his room, we stocked it with Dr. Peppers (which he loves). We fixed a big bowl of peanut-better crackers on the table by his bed. Then we hung family pictures.

NOVEMBER 17, 2008

Today I walked in, and he was watching Judge Judy and just loving it and talking back to her. This is the best he has been at the hospital. He talked really well and wanted to go—somewhere. Anyway, I stayed until dinnertime, and he seemed to enjoy it. Maybe things will start looking up. His spirits seem so much better.

NOVEMBER 18, 2008

When I got there, he was talking to another man in a wheelchair and seemed to be making a friend. They just really seemed to be enjoying each other. They were down by the nurses' station, and he didn't want to quit visiting the man to talk with me. That's good. The nurses said the man is named

Sam, and he is blind but doesn't know it. And he doesn't look blind. Although Sam has had a bad stroke, he's a cheerful, happy man. As we were watching TV, the recreation director came in and talked to us. Bill still can't answer questions like what year it is, what the date is, where he lives, how many children he has, or anything like that. But he can sure pass it off by saying, "Oh, it doesn't matter" or "I don't really care." His spirits are so much better, and he seems happy.

NOVEMBER 19, 2008

I was there a long time today, and he was talking really well. His new doctor came by. I like him very much. He talks straight. He told me that Bill's test showed that he has had three ministrokes, and that a large white mass had shown up in the images in his head. He asked if he had ever had a bad head injury, and I told him that Bill had been in a bad car accident while in college. The car rolled over and landed on his head, breaking his jaw in two places. It was terrible. The doctor said that the head injury was probably the cause of what he was seeing on the electrocardiograms. The doctor is starting him on B12 shots once a week and then we'll go to once a month.

Bill pulled his catheter out at about five o'clock this morning. It must have been terribly painful. He bled quite a bit. He's very sore and has scabs on his head. The doctor prescribed all kinds of things and special medicine for his head. He left orders that they are to wash his hair with a special shampoo every other day, and he told them to keep his hair trimmed neatly. With his hair cut short I can doctor it better, and so can the nurses.

Bill seems pretty settled in. I left $60 for activities, but I doubt that he does much. He didn't want me to leave. His eyes just light up whenever I come in, and he looks so sad when I leave. Maybe they can get him leveled out with the meds, and I can bring him home and get some good help and keep him at home where we can be together. I really think I can take better care of him if I just have full-time help. I think anyone is better off at home, and I know he would be more contented. I guess we'll just have to see what's down the road and not rush it.

At home, I did get rid of the big king-size bed and got two little twin beds. I just couldn't look at it, but these will be good for when he comes home. They told me Medicare will pay for some help. If not, I will manage one way or another.

NOVEMBER 21, 2008

I feel very strongly that I am right that I could do a better job taking care of him at home. I worked on his hair some more today. He had on a dirty shirt, so I changed that and cleaned him up. It's so sad: we didn't talk much. We just watched TV, and I worked at getting him neater and cleaner. I must talk to the head nurse again on keeping him cleaner.

NOVEMBER 24, 2008

All weekend has been quiet. Bill has been blind in his left eye since childhood, and today his bad eye was matted. I soaked it with warm cloths and washed it. I'll bring his good drops to keep here. His color was not good. He seems to be going downhill again. I called the psychiatrist, and he was supposed to call at 11:00 a.m. but didn't. So I called at 11:30. I had to leave as I had five loans to get to the main office in Corpus Christi, and the nurse said the doctor would call me after 4:00 p.m.

I ran to Corpus Christi as quickly as I could and got back and sat by the phone waiting. No call at all. I missed seeing Bill. I hate that, but I felt I really had to talk to the doctor. I don't want to change doctors, but I want to make sure I can get all his medications when I bring him home. I want to discuss everything now so I can be getting ready.

NOVEMBER 25, 2008

No phone call, dammit.

NOVEMBER 26, 2008

I went early, and Bill was listening to music. I said, "Honey, let's go to your room. I want to tell you something." I couldn't wait to tell him I planned to bring him home. I could tell he didn't want to leave the entertainment, but I wheeled him down to his room, closed the door, cleaned his eye and said, "Bill, I am working on bringing you home in January, and I will talk to the doctor again this week and see if we can get a home health nurse to come by and give the shots and medicine. I can get you bathed and dressed and you will be home with me and Sugar." He just looked at me like I was nuts or something and said nothing. Then I said, "Well, the doctor said I have to get all the guns out of the house, and you can't drive your pickup anymore. But we can do that." He still didn't say anything.

You could hear the awful music through the door. He said, "Oh, I like that tune." He didn't say a word about what I said. I just looked at him and asked, "Do you want to go listen to the music?" He said, "Yeah." So I rolled him down and he just loved it. It was really bad music. He even threw his hands in the air when they played and sang "I'll Fly Away." He enjoyed it so much. He was in a clean shirt; his scalp was still needing medicine, but he was better. Everyone was off for Thanksgiving, so I really couldn't bitch. I'll handle that next week. He would just listen to the music and pat my leg, keeping time with the music. I then patted his arm, and he looked straight at me and said, "Don't touch me." Hmmm. Can't figure it out.

We sat there at least another hour and half, and he would listen to the music and close his eyes. Then opened them suddenly and looked at me, and said, "You know there wouldn't be a problem at all if they matched the dogs to their names: the silly nuts don't know anything." I felt like the silly nut.

Can't wait to talk to the doctor. I realize more and more that I must be able to make a sensible, good decision and do what is truly best for Bill. I can't do what I want the most or what is best for me. Now I am wondering whether he is better taken care of here and is enjoying the entertainment more than he would at home. They do have a regular routine, and I know that it is a good place. I also know that he would push me into letting him do the things he wanted and do as he pleased at home. And I know he can't make decisions or do logical things. I couldn't stand it if he started wandering and heading to Amarillo again. They told me to give it 90 days to really see how it is going at the home, how he is adjusting, and what they can do for him. The food is exceptionally good (for a home), and they have entertainment all the time—much more than most rest homes. This home is privately owned, and they do a lot of extras even though the cost is the about the same at all the homes—in other words, no discounts, no cheapies. I am going to catch that damn doctor after Thanksgiving if I have to camp out on his front door.

Bill tried and tried to button his shirt and can't button anymore. He has pulled all the strings out of his warm-up pants and now they are nearly falling off. He hid the strings so we'll have to get some other kinds of pants that don't require belts or strings—some kind of elastic waist.

DECEMBER 1, 2008

It was so cold today, and I got here early. Bill was sitting in his chair with his eyes closed. I had a meeting with Dee, the administrator, and told her that I knew they hadn't given him his pills a few times, and that he had to have them. I like her very much. I also told her I was trying for some extra insurance, and she said she would help on that. She gave me some other places to check where I might get some financial help. She suggested I move him to a cheaper room (with a roommate) and I said, "No way." I laughed and said I will work a little harder.

I have made friends with Fae, Sam's wife. Her husband, remember, is the blind man in the wheelchair—the one who'd had a stroke. He is the friend that Bill enjoys the most. Sam is from Laredo, Texas, and Bill is from Amarillo, Texas, and they talk about their towns all the time. It doesn't make sense to listen to them, but they agree and just laugh.

Bill has settled in pretty well but still doesn't want me to leave—and he's not talking much. I asked him when his birthday is, and he said 1911. I held a picture of Toni and asked who it was, and he said "Bebe." He thinks all the pictures of Toni are me. I think he remembers my looking like that when I was young. He is just always so happy to see me, but now I have to slip off when I'm leaving. I am feeling like he is in a really good place.

We're still doctoring his head, and he is getting thinner. His neck is so small now. Still, something that happened today has lifted my spirits: one of the nurses told me they are all in love with him, that he is so sweet, and doesn't complain.

I will miss tomorrow, as I have to go to Beeville for work—to make every dime I can. When I told them I wouldn't be there tomorrow, they said, "Actually, it is better if you don't come every day. We can get Bill adjusted better when you aren't here so much. It would be better if you came only about three times a week." Well, that isn't going to happen.

Prayerful Bombardments

Although I missed yesterday, Bill didn't even know it. The doctor was there today and said Bill had a bad sore on his tailbone, and they are treating it. I took a feather pillow over for him to sit on. He has another cough and can't get over it. The doctor said he is having a hard time swallowing; he'll be checking on that some more. Bill isn't eating much but snacks on the peanut-butter crackers. Sometimes he'll eat only two, but he loves them. He used to eat the whole pack.

He talked a little more today—nothing big. It's just that he didn't like that belt on him, and he didn't like some lady who keeps coming up to him. When she came in, he told her to get out and leave him alone. I asked him his birthday again today and he said October 5, 1929. It's the first time he's gotten that right. He didn't say anything else, but . . . .

I had seen the doctor first and was talking to him when Bill saw me and started wheeling toward me and grabbed my hand. He is so cute and so very happy to see me—it sure makes his day for me just to be there, so I like to be there even if we don't talk. I feel he is being well taken care of. The doctor told me he had observed Bill going up and down all the halls all the time. He laughed and said he really moves around.

DECEMBER 4, 2008

Well, this was really a day. I got there and couldn't find Bill anywhere, although everyone said they had just seen him. They had been down every hall, but hadn't opened all the doors. I was going like mad calling, "Bill! Bill!" I was really getting worried. Then, about four doors down past his room, they found him in a little lady's room. He had his foot in her lap and was really giving her orders. He was telling her to put his shoe on, and he was saying all she had to do was push, push, push. "You can do better! PUSH!" The little lady looked so pitiful, and said, "I'm trying, but my wrist is broken and I can't get this shoe on. He is getting mad at me." I said, "Well, that's okay, I'll put it on for him, thanks so much." She kept holding her wrist and saying, "Oh, my wrist hurts so much." Of course the nurses are all used to this.

I took Bill to his room and slipped his shoes on and said, "Bill, you shouldn't go in other people's rooms." He looked up at me and said, "Well, I'm getting out of this automobile-tractor and going to lie down on my side." I said, "Well, I don't think you can because you are strapped in the chair." He said, "Hand me a knife and I can cut it." I said, "No we have to have a key and it's up at the desk." He got quite angry at the chair and finally started snapping his fingers at me and said, "Get me the damn key, Bebe."

Instead, I started showing him pictures and of course he didn't know any of us. He thought Toni was me and Suzanne was Sally—Sally who, I have no idea. He called Mitch "Abner" and looked at Tye a long time and said, "Well, that's him," pointing to another big picture of Tye on the wall.

Then he put the picture basket down on the bed and leaned over and put his head in the basket. I said, "Bill, what are you doing?" He said, "Shut up, I'm praying." So I shut up, thinking what a wonderful thing that was. When he finally raised his head, I said, "Well, honey, what did you pray for?" He looked me right in the eye and said he prayed that the atomic bomb would drop on my head. Well, so much for the holy feelings and my feeling that he had found the Lord. I laughed again. Better to laugh than take it in the spirit it came in.

He was really something else today. I wheeled him down to dinner and he saw they were having hamburgers and fries—his favorite. So I slipped out. We'll see what tomorrow brings. I think I had better do the praying from now on.

DECEMBER 7, 2008

Today, as soon as I went into his room, he wanted some ice to chew on. I went down and got some while he was watching a motorcycle movie with daredevil tricks. He liked it so much. He wanted me to get him out of the chair, and I did and let him get on the recliner—just like the old Bill. While relaxing, all propped up on his pillows, hanging his leg off the side—he has never sat in a chair like other people or propped up like others—he reached for my hands, dozed off holding on tight, and wouldn't let go. In a little while, he said, "I'm gonna line up 20 quarter horses, and I want all you girls to pick one out. When I say Go we'll see who wins, and you have to be first." Hmmm.

I was watching a young girl (who's totally out of it) going down the hall cradling Louisiana Hot Sauce bottles against her chest, so I mentioned it to the aide who was near. She said, "Oh yeah, she takes all she can carry out of the dining room every day. We just go get them back. They all take stuff. Bill does too, and he hides it." Sure enough, when I went back in Bill's room I looked though his dresser drawers and found packets and packets of salt, pepper, sugar, and creamer. He doesn't even use these. I asked Bill why he had all this stuff because they have plenty in the dining room. He looked at me like I was crazy and said, "Shhh—don't tell them. I got this for you and me." I told the girls and they just laughed and said, "Well, at least he isn't on the hot sauce."

One lady, about 85, was crying for her mother and wailing, "Mother, Mother, where are you? I'm here." She looked at me and said, "My mother is looking for me." Just then the aide came over and said, "Remember, your mother is working very hard to take care of everyone, and she is resting, so just wait a while now." I thought, Well that was a good answer. Because dumb me—when Bill had wanted to call his mother when he was still home, I told him she was dead and it sent him into a terrible depression. Finally he had said, "You may be right." I sure didn't know the right answers.

Bill is very satisfied and well taken care of. It's just amazing how flat his stomach is. It is as flat as the day we married. He is very thin, though. All that bad urine is out, but now he is having more trouble swallowing.

I guess I have learned one thing: it is out of my hands— I am going to let the Lord guide me from now on. And I'm truly thankful for a really good long marriage and fun with the man I love. It's been 55 years now, and I thank God for the man who taught me how to shoot deer from the highest mountain in Wyoming, discovered New Orleans with me (all the way down the river five times), taught me deep-sea fishing, and took care of me through eleven miscarriages. He loved my family; he considered my only brother Tom his brother also; he gave me my own little cotton patch in 1954. Those 13 acres down on the creek bottom proved a real boon: after making $2,000 on that little project, I invested in Shetland ponies, wound up with eight little mares and one little stallion (38" tall). Bill told people he was keeping me busy. We had so much fun and laughed together the whole time. I had so much fun. When I learned we were going to be parents in 1959, we sold our horses. Our baby girl with the big brown eyes was born on May 5, 1959, followed by a baby boy in 1960.

Times were good for the Bralleys. It rained on the Groom ranch and the Silverton farm, oil prices were going up, and my dad and Bill bought 1,000 feeder lambs that the army bought as soon as they were ready for market. There was never a boring moment. We had great friends and were blessed with three more children (two boys, in 1960 and 1964, and another girl in 1968). Luck has pretty much stayed with us for almost 53 years. Later, we had a long-term lease with the Texas National Guard that never interfered with the cattle business, but it paid for some college tuitions. No one could beat the fun, laughs, and very, very fortunate life we have had. But all things have to end, or so the story goes—we can't plan the end, but no regrets for me.

DECEMBER 8, 2008

Bill was very quiet today and didn't feel good. The nurses are so sweet to him, and he has them wrapped around his finger. He is a good patient. Bill loves to sit at the nurses' station in his wheelchair and chew ice. They tell me he is no trouble and they love him. He doesn't eat much at all, and he's so thin. He's still having a hard time swallowing—one of the symptoms of Alzheimer's.

The nurses were all decorating for Christmas, and he sat right with them in the middle of it all. The Christmas music was so loud I thought I would get a headache, but they all seemed to be loving it and just dancing to the tunes. Some of the patients were clapping and singing right along.

Bill seemed cold, so I will buy a sweater. He has never been a sweater-wearer so maybe one of those warmup tops will work. If it has a hood on it, I'll just whack it off. He would hate a hood.

DECEMBER 9, 2008

As we watched Judge Judy, Bill cussed at her just like he used to when he thought she had made the wrong decision. He was sort of his old self. Someone brought a small bowl of fruit—apples, oranges, and grapes. When I asked him where he got the pretty fruit, he pointed up and said, "It just came from up there somewhere."

When I took him down for dinner, thinking I'd slip away, he threw a fit for the first time in a long time. He held on to my arm and said, "No, you can't go. Don't go. Don't go." The aide had to take his arm off me and distract him. When he looked the other way, I ran for the door. I felt terrible. He is just like the kids used to be when they didn't want to stay with a babysitter. But he thinks this is home now, or rather a nice motel, and he wants me there all the time. I hate that part.

DECEMBER 10, 2008

Well, glory be. The doctor called. I nearly fainted. I have waited so long and gotten so mad—it is usually his assistant who calls and says, "Oh, he will call after 4:00 or sometime." I said right off, "Since I now have you on the phone, I don't want to waste your time. I want some straight answers." I started with When could I bring him home and What do I expect in the future and Are we improving his health now?

Well, I will give the doctor credit because he shot right back with straight answers starting off by saying, "You ask for straight. Okay, Bill is at the end of Alzheimer's. You ask me, I will tell you. He will continue to deteriorate more all the time. There is no turning back or cure. He needs full-time care at all times, and you cannot give him that at home. He has mood swings and will continue to. That is another reason you cannot have him at home—it is not safe for you or others.

"I have him medicated to keep him from being so agitated, but I do not and will not overmedicate. It sometimes changes day to day, even hour to hour, and has to fit the feeling he has that day. Only professionals can judge that. The nurses do not have the right to just give medication that is not prescribed, but they have the freedom to call me—or another doctor—anytime they can't handle a situation.

"Bill has a tendency not to re-direct (Lord, don't I know that!), so I must keep him where he is calm and comfortable, not abusive or agitated, and on a very regular schedule. If this can't be done in the rest home, the only other place would be the state sanatorium in Austin or Big Spring, Texas. But I truly believe we can keep him well and contented with proper medication and care where he is. He has not been abusive to others here. If he should be abusive to the staff, we can still work with him. But if he should be abusive to other patients, we would have to remove him.

"I will be seeing him each week, and I strongly advise that you do not take him out for home visits or dinners. I know most patients go for day-long or weekend visits, and that is usually good. But Bill is not one of them.

"We now have him on a regular routine, and we need to keep on that same routine each day of his life. Bill has the judgment of a 3-year-old, so he doesn't know what is dangerous. He doesn't know how to react to anything on his own.

"I see patients in many homes, and I can tell you that you have him in the best home for him that I know of. The caretakers here are exceptional and have all been here a long time. They care about their patients and stay updated on all the latest training and information on Alzheimer's."

He also told me he had arranged for Bill to go to another internist on the 18th because he can hardly swallow anything now. Bill is losing weight too fast. He ended by saying that with this disease, we cannot tell how long a patient has. Usually death comes from something else.

I had just gotten back to my home when this call came. It was very cold today, and I took Bill more warmups. The other doctor was at the home when I got there, and I was happy to get to see him. He had put Bill on a liquid diet and a few very soft foods. They are feeding him in a separate dining room now, for the people who are very, very sick. I call them the end-of-the-line people. The nurse stepped over and said, "We are also scrambling him some eggs and stuff like that to fill him up."

Today he asked me if we got all the hogs in, and I said, "Yeah." He said, "Well, what about down at the end of the channel?" I said, "Don't worry, it is all taken care of." He sat quiet for a while and then looked at me and said, "Well, let's get out of here and do our thing." I laughed and said, "Okay— in just a little while. That's a good idea." Bill looked right at me and said, "Hell yes, it's a good idea."

I don't think he'll like eating in that special room. He likes the big dining room, and sitting with his buddies. I went by Tye's house to tell him about Bill and told him no visitors except family, as I know he will help.

Today Mr. Houdini, otherwise known as Bill Bralley, while strapped in his chair, got out of it and pulled it over on himself. Supposedly no one can get out of them. That's the point: to keep somebody in a chair where they can't get out. But this wasn't the first time. Yesterday, when I got there, he had one leg out again and fell. They found him on the floor with the chair on top of him. I know they thought I would be mad. I just said, "No surprise to me. When Bill Bralley sets his head to do something, he will figure out a way." I looked right at him and said, "Bill, don't get out of the chair unless the girls get you out." Again he looked at me like I'm the crazy one.

Thinking in a Different Key

It is so cold that I bought a lot more warmups for him. When I got there, I couldn't find him anywhere. We all looked and finally found him in the last room down the opposite wing from his room. When they were bringing him out, he looked up and saw me said, "Well, there you are. I have been looking for you everywhere. All over town." He said Jackie Fuqua was there and he brought some fruit. I said, "Well, that was nice. How is Jackie?" And he said, "Oh, he died." Then he talked about some people that are trying to get us to buy something, but he said he knew it was a trick. He said, "You know some people just don't think too well." I said, "Yeah, I know."

There is an old woman who turns around and around in circles. Her mind is obviously blank. Her poor head hangs down, and she looks pitiful. Bill pointed to her and said, "I can't stand her." I said, "Well, she is probably very nice." Bill said, "Oh no she isn't! But you know what?" I said, "What?" He said, "She is smart as a whip and doesn't want anyone to know it!" I just said, "Well, my goodness. You'd sure never know it." Bill looked at me like I just don't understand life and said, "Bebe, you have to watch 'em around here. They will fool you." Then he just looked off, and that was it for the day.

DECEMBER 12, 2008

Tye had gone early this morning and met with Bill for breakfast. They had a good visit. Bill was tickled to see him and they talked about Salty, Bill's favorite horse at the ranch, and working on corrals. Tye had brought papers with deer and hunting information, and although Bill can't read anymore, Tye said he enjoyed the wildlife pictures. According to Tye and the nurses, Bill is always better in the morning. He seems to go downhill after lunch. That was happening at home, too.

I went at 4:00 p.m.; Suzanne had been there an hour earlier. Comparing our information showed that there was big difference. Betty, the head nurse who Bill loves dearly, led singing today and they were singing Christmas songs and all enjoying that. I stayed until 5:00 p.m., and we watched Frank Sinatra. Bill loved that.

He can't control his bladder, so that's a constant problem. They handle it pretty well, but he still stays so chapped and raw that he needs the diapers changed more often. He said he had a good visit with Dorset, a dear friend and brother-in-law. I asked what happened and he looked at me funny and said, "Well, you should know; you were right there riding with us all day." I said, "Oh yeah."

DECEMBER 13, 2008

I had a big day ahead of me cleaning house, so I went to the home early. Bill was wandering barefoot. I asked where his shoes were and the nurse said, "We don't know. He has been in every room in the home today and kicked his shoes off two or three times. His socks, too." I said, "Bill, let's go look for your shoes. Finally he said, "No, let's just go home. Dorset was here all day, and we worked on his damn plane. I told him it had to have water in the . . . well, you know what . . . he wouldn't listen to me. Finally I just said, 'Well, to hell with it,' and left Dorset standing right there."

I am switching him to a newer brand of Depends that may help with the chafing. They say there is no difference, but I think there is. We watched TV. He seemed to enjoy it. It was a train show, and he immediately wanted us to go on a train trip. Of course, I said we would. I took him down to dinner and had to slip out again, as he didn't want me to leave and was kind of watching me close. But one of the aides got his attention.

DECEMBER 16, 2008

Today was the Christmas party. The staff worked really hard putting on the show. They had a cross-eyed scrubby-looking guitar player and an over-bleached blonde who looked like she'd been in an entirely different line of business before this show. It was so very loud. Every other song was a fast Spanish song. One little Hispanic lady got so excited she jumped right out of her wheelchair and fell flat on her face—before her daughter could catch her—and she kept singing. They all got excited. Bill clapped and would shout "Olé!"

Then he started worrying that we didn't have enough money to get us out of this joint. I said, "Yeah, we do." Then he said, "Well, where's the car? We may have to make a run for it. I've seen this kind of crowd before." I said we were pretty close in but could sure make a run for it. Then they played "In the Mood." (That's almost a sin to say they *played* it.) It was an awful rendition, but Bill loved that and said, "Remember?" And I did. He started winding down but kept worrying about getting us paid up and out. Finally I said, "You wait right here and I'll go and pay, and then we can make a run for it." I went to his nurse and said "Bill's played out and ready for bed." She took over and I slipped out.

DECEMBER 17, 2008

Today was sad. Tye and I got there at nearly the same time, and when we walked in the nurse said, "Thank God you're here! Bill thinks you are dead!" I went into his room and put my arms around him and said, "Hi baby, I'm here." He looked up and tears were streaming down his face. I'd so seldom seen Bill cry. He said, "I thought you were dead, and I can't live without you. Oh Bebe! Oh Bebe!" He held on to me for so long. And I said, "Oh Bill, you will always have me." I tried to make him smile.

When Tye came in, Bill told him about his fear that I'd died. Tye immediately started trying to make his Daddy smile. He would say, "Mom's okay. Don't worry, Dad. I check on her all the time, and always will." Tye is so good to get him onto other things. Then he looked at Tye and said, "I made a list for us." (Of course he can't write.) He was talking kind of crazy, but Tye went along with it just as if they were going down a list of things to do.

Finally, Bill was okay and looked at me and just said: "I'm so glad you're here. I just knew you were dead." Tomorrow we go to Corpus to the doctor. I'll meet Bill and Big Vicki over there. She's a jewel who knows just how to handle Bill. We both love her.

DECEMBER 18, 2008

Long day. I met Bill and Big Vicki. She's the driver for the home. She said Bill kept asking her the whole time whether they were nearly to Amarillo. "Will my sweetheart be there?" (He calls me his sweetheart all the time now—not his wife.) Big Vicki is sassy and strong as an ox. She can handle Bill all by herself.

We were there from morning until almost 6. They asked Bill the same old questions except for one new one: Are you a Democrat or Republican? Bill looked up and smiled and said, "Republican." Everyone laughed at that. I felt so sorry for him, though, because the doctor would ask questions and he'd look to me for answers. But they had told me beforehand that I couldn't say a word or I'd have to leave the room. Next time, I think I'll just ask not to be in the room because he depends on me. I feel awful when I feel like I've let him down.

He was so tired but still had to make the trip all the way back to Rockport. After Vicki and Bill left, the doctor called me in and said, "Bebe, I think we'll have to put a feeding tube in his stomach. We'll need you to sign the permission paper as that may be his only way to get food." I said, "No, I won't sign. I won't allow it. We can run more tests and just figure out something else. We are all tired tonight. But Bill couldn't stand that. And I couldn't either. We are not going there."

DECEMBER 19, 2008

Liz, our daughter-in-law, made Bill a pretty Christmas tree for his room. It looks so pretty. He was very quiet today and slept a lot. He's tired from yesterday. He has a terrible rash.

DECEMBER 20, 2008

They had music today. Thank God he wasn't very interested. It was an old man and woman who sang a lot of old songs, which didn't go over too well with anyone. They were just plain awful. But you've got to give them credit: they were doing it free and trying to help out. Bill's stomach was hurting. I slipped out while he was sleeping.

DECEMBER 21, 2008

Today was the birthday of our youngest daughter, Suzanne. I told him, but it didn't ring much of a bell. I said, "Can you believe it's been 40 years?" He looked at me and said, "Does she know?" I said, "Yes, she knows it's her birthday." He said, "Well, good." Then he turned and looked away. He didn't like his chair, and his rash hurt.

DECEMBER 22, 2008

I swear he was so normal today. I thought he might be snapping out of it. Maybe it could happen. We watched an old Bette Davis show and he knew every movie star in the film. He lay back on the bed, propped up, and really watched. I wondered whether maybe things were coming back. So in a little while I asked whether he knew what month this is. "Remember? There are Santas everywhere and trees and elves—everything Christmas." He looked at me (as if feeling sorry for me) and said, "Don't you know?"

Then a little later he told me Jackie Fuqua had taken over the other side of the building and that he'd let him take it over. He said he told Jackie that he'd better let him go over when he wanted to. I asked what Jackie had said. "Well, you know Fuqua." That's when I decided he wasn't getting quite as normal as I had hoped.

We did have fun today, and he was propped up swinging his leg over the side like he always has. I sat in the wheelchair and propped my feet up by his. We ate a peanut-butter cracker and drank Dr. Pepper. It was nice. He didn't like it when I said, "Well, it's your turn to get in the chair and we'll go to dinner." Finally, he said we'd sit right by each other and eat together. I had to do the old slip-out thing again.

DECEMBER 24, 2008

Bill was very listless today and said he felt really bad. He just laid his head on the table and didn't talk at all. He just held my hand. I could tell he felt awful. I doctored the rash a little extra today. It's just too many things at once.

DECEMBER 25, 2008

Went to Suzanne's to see little Ben be surprised by Santa. He's our youngest grandchild and such a joy. Bill would have loved that. He has always loved little children and gets a kick out of them. I went on to see Bill, and he was looking for me when I got there. I hollered at him as I could see him way down the hall—where he is not supposed to be. He looked in my direction, but I could tell he didn't know it was me. Then, when I got closer, he shouted loudly, "Beeeebeee! I didn't think you would ever find me!" He grabbed me and held me so long. He got tears in his eyes and said, "I thought I was someplace where you wouldn't ever find me. How did you find me?" He just held on to me too tightly. I took us to a little table and chairs, and we sat down while he was holding both my hands and I said, "Bill I will always find you." He said, "Promise?" I said, "Promise."

This day made me realize how terrible it must be not to know where you are or what's happening, and to remember only one person—then thinking that person can't find you. It breaks my heart. I just feel so sorry for him. He's lost all the time. He doesn't even know how to turn around and go back to his room. It amazes me that he even knows he is lost.

DECEMBER 26, 2008

Bill didn't feel good today. His back and stomach hurt. He just felt bad all over. He loves to eat ice. I think that's good because he doesn't drink much water. As I rubbed his back, he told me who he liked and didn't like. (No names—just descriptions.) One man who's in a terrible shape he really didn't like. I said, "Well, he's really sick and he's had all his toes all cut off." Bill said, "Well, I think he stuck his toe in the wrong place anyway."

More music today. It was a young man and two stringy-haired girls. They tried their best, but gosh, they were awful. I have to give them credit for not giving up. They sang their hearts out. Even Bill said they weren't much good. Then he said, "Do we have to listen to them?" I said no, we'd get out of there. I said, "Let's go to the patio and get some sunshine." He liked that, but then he got worried that some robbers would come and steal "everything we have," so we went back in and it was nearly dinnertime.

DECEMBER 27, 2008

Bill's feet are really swollen. He was quiet. He felt so bad that he never got out of bed. Finally, he ate a few peanut-butter crackers and drank some Dr. Pepper.

DECEMBER 28, 2008

His feet are very swollen. The nurses had put his slippers on and the heel was so tight it rubbed his heel raw. I took it right off and soothed his feet with cream and told them to leave off the slippers until the swelling went down. I asked them to call the podiatrist and make an appointment for him to look at his feet and trim his nails. He is sore in his crotch and has an infection on his hip that simply won't clear up. I'm waiting to see another doctor.

Bill hasn't talked all day. He just held my hands. Then he opened his eyes and said, "I have a new rule: You cannot be gone longer than 20 minutes. Then you come right back to me." I took him down to dinner and had to pull the old slip-away. I hate that, but he has an absolute fit if he knows I'm leaving. And he doesn't care who hears him.

DECEMBER 29, 2008

I didn't go today but closed five loans. (I need the money.) Yeah. It was a really hectic day. Tye went and walked him a little and said his feet weren't quite as swollen as yesterday.

We'll see another doctor tomorrow. It's getting to the end of a year I haven't liked.

DECEMBER 30, 2008

We watched a John Wayne movie. He liked that. He slept most of the time today.

DECEMBER 31 2008

Well, thank God 2008 is over. I'm glad. It has hit everyone in the family hard. In lots of ways. David, our son-in-law, had heart surgery in March. Mitch lost his job (but got another one the same week). The economy is very bad. And Bill has definitely gone downhill all year. Never did I think this time last year that Bill would be in a home this New Year's Eve. This year has gone faster than I ever dreamed, and I had had such hopes for good things to happen. We sure didn't get that house in Port Aransas that we had planned for. Maybe next year will be better.

They had little hats and horns for all the patients, and Bill listened to the music and had ice cream and cake. It's sure different from the way we used to celebrate New Year's Eve. Wow, what good times we've had; I do believe the most memorable one was in Salt Lake City in 1957. We had been deer hunting for a week on one of the highest mountains in Afton, Wyoming, with a great guide (also named Bill). We stayed at a great lodge that had no entertainment but a great restaurant and bar where everyone gathered for hunting stories in the evening. My feet had gotten frostbite, and Bill rubbed and rubbed them for hours to get the circulation going again. Still, we enjoyed everything so much, went to bed early each night so we could be up before dawn to start on the hunts. When we left we were ready to party and thought Salt Lake City would be a blast, so we headed that way. We didn't know they had no bars, nightclubs, or liquor stores. What a shock. Bill finally found a taxi driver who knew a place he could get us into for $50, so off we went. For another $20 he got us our favorite Schlitz beer. We've always celebrated New Year's Eve in a big way and had a ball each time, usually with everyone winding up at the ranch the next day. But Salt Lake City was the one that really stands out. We have laughed about that one for years. We couldn't even get a hangover. So yeah—the times have changed. At least I am still with my favorite man of all time.

Farewell 2008.

2009

A YEAR OF CONFINEMENT— WITH ONE LAST TRIP

"What's Happening to Me?"

I missed the last few days as David, our son-in-law, was in the hospital. They took Bill for another sonogram with the doctor in Corpus Christi on Friday. I won't know anything for a few days. Today Bill was facing the wall, tied in his chair, and not very alert. He was very disoriented and didn't know me at first. When I got closer to him he was happy to see me, and wanted to know where he was. I took him to his room and changed his Depends; he had to change them again in less than 10 minutes. He doesn't look good and can't comprehend anything at all.

After getting him in bed, I put a movie on as that helps sometimes. It was about a hotel fire. All of a sudden he got in a fetal position and said, "Oh Bebe, Bebe. We will never get out. I am so scared. We are going to burn to death. I am so scared. Hurry!" I quickly turned it off and covered him good and held him tight. It had upset him so much. He was very cold, and after wrapping him up and getting him all warm he dozed off to sleep. I stayed and woke him for dinner. He was fine and remembered nothing about the fire. I said, "David is in the hospital and very sick." He said, "Yeah, I read that in the paper." He seems to have gone downhill the last two days.

JANUARY 4, 2009

Bill was in his chair in the lobby and very disoriented and was shaking quite a bit. He asked me, "What's happening to me? I feel so bad. I am sick." I said, "Yes, you are." I started to push him to his room. When I tried to push the chair, he wouldn't raise his feet. He just held that one place, it was like trying to push cement. I said, "Honey, you have to lift your feet." He still didn't, and wouldn't. I literally shoved his chair into his room and thought I would drop. I still don't know why he wouldn't lift his feet. He will usually do what I say, but not this time. He wanted to lie down, so I unhooked him, and he acted like he didn't know how to get up out of the chair. I pulled on him and finally got him in bed. Then a silly TV show came on and he watched a little. I got some ice for him to chew on.

Finally, the girl came by and said, "Time for dinner." I finally pulled him up and had the chair right against him. I said, "Okay, now sit." He wouldn't. I tried to gently push him, and nothing—he wouldn't budge. He started getting frustrated and said, "What the hell do you want me to do?" I said, "I want you to sit down in the chair, Bill." He said, "Well, I don't know what you mean. You don't talk sense. I'm about to fall down." We kept doing that until finally he fell on the bed. I said, "Well, stay right here." I ran and got a male nurse. He said, "I can get him in the chair." By that time I was worn out and just hoping they got him to dinner.

I think he may have had another little stroke today. His eyes were not clear, he was totally out of it, and his mouth hung down on one side. He said silly words that didn't make real words. Then he went back to the whispers.

JANUARY 5, 2009

Today is Tye's birthday. I baked his favorite cake—the Watergate cake—and dropped it by his house on the way to see Bill. When I got there Bill was only halfway on the bed with his legs tied up in the wheelchair ropes. He was wet all over. I called the aide, who got him untied and put dry clothes on him. Apparently he had tried to get himself some water and spilled it all over himself, while thinking he could get out of the chair. He just keeps forgetting that he's in a wheelchair.

Completely exhausted, he said he felt bad. The main nurse came in and said he'd been sick the night before and the doctor had put him on antibiotics because he was running a high fever. He has a dry cough but can't spit up anything. When he finally lay down, I got some ice for him to chew on.

When I woke him up for dinner he said, "No, no, I can't eat. I don't want to get up." So I called the nurse, who brought some soup so that I could feed him in bed. We just had to get something in him. I propped him up on pillows since we're trying to ward off pneumonia. He is weak and looks really sick. His eyes aren't clear, and his lips are a bluish white. Maybe he'll feel better tomorrow.

JANUARY 6, 2009

I got a call at 12:15 last night. They had to rush Bill to Northbay Hospital. The nurse told me not to come then, just to wait until morning. If I'm needed, they'll call. They did call me later, at barely 6:00 a.m. Bill has a severe kidney infection, so I'm going to be staying with him. Bill looks so bad, his fever is very high, he's on oxygen, and he doesn't like that oxygen one bit. When Tye and Suzanne came, I went home for a little while.

When I returned I found that Mitch and Shirley had been there for about two hours, taking turns with him. He was shaking a lot and looked yellow. Jaundiced. He asked Tye for a Pepsi. We laughed at that. Tye went and got a Pepsi. Bill took a few sips and said, "Oh-h-h this is soo-o-o good." He's freezing, but later the nurses took all the covers off and said he needs to be cooler because his fever is still going up so much. It had started up again just a little while ago. He is so thin and yellow.

He seemed more alert today than in a long time—he knew all of us, and you could tell he was really glad to see us all. But he was exhausted, and he'd doze off. He's been in so much pain today, we'll see what tomorrow brings. I'm kind of scared to face tomorrow.

JANUARY 7, 2009

Bill is a lot worse today than ever before. His cheeks are drawn and his face ashen-white, but with ruddy cheeks. His hands are grayish and white. His legs are yellow. He seems to have no life left in him. He doesn't turn his head. To me this seems the worst day. He still has a high fever, and he's not eating even soup. The nurse is going to try to get some baby food down him tonight. But I'm going to bring some of my homemade chicken soup tonight. That always helps.

JANUARY 8, 2009

He ate my soup (a little bit), and he's better this morning. He had just finished his bath and couldn't even hold his head up he was so weak. And he's pale. Suzanne and I helped him to the bed from his chair. He simply couldn't move on his own. He just lay flat. They had to put the oxygen back on, and he didn't like that. He kept trying to pull it off, but he didn't really have the strength.

The nurses there love him. They said he's sweet and doesn't complain. But he would not let the aide shave him.

He's really too tired for that. I went home to rest a little, and when I got back, they had moved the blood-pressure machine. His BP was 112/70—too low. Whenever I ask how he is, the nurses always say, "Oh, about the same." I get tired of that.

At 6 he'd actually eaten some food—nearly a third of the plate. It was all soft food, but he ate it. The nurse had to feed him, and he didn't like that. But he ate like he was hungry. When she put him up in the chair, he started trying to pull the catheter out, but couldn't; she was watching him closely and said, she would be putting him to bed soon. She'd knock him out so he can sleep. That'll stop him from pulling the catheter out.

Although he still looks bad, he's more alert: he knew me and was irritated with the nurse. At least that got him talking. He is usually worse in the evening, but he seemed better tonight.

JANUARY 10, 2009

Much better today. He's started eating a little more. Real food. And he seems to be more alert. He still has a stomach-ache and the catheter. He told me that he went to town this morning, where it was quite cold, and that he saw the biggest cat he'd ever seen, but he didn't go up to it because it looked really mean. A man told Bill he was studying the cat to find out what kind it was. Hmmm.

JANUARY 11, 2009

Bill looked so much better today. Mitch and Shirley were there, but he was asleep while they were there. He was disappointed to learn that he'd missed them. He asked, "Will they come back?" I said yes. I noticed today that the left side of his mouth seems to droop a little, and his left hand is completely numb. He couldn't feel anything when I pinched it, and he didn't feel anything when the nurse put ice cubes on him. When I rubbed and rubbed his hands, he looked at me and said, "It's all right, Bebe." I'm worried that his lip is hanging down. I think he's had another ministroke. I'll tell the doctor and show him a picture. I'm told he'll be going back to his usual room tomorrow. Maybe the infections are taken care of.

Unpredictable Befallings

JANUARY 12, 2009

They released Bill to his usual room about 3:30 today. He's so worn out. Very weak. Didn't talk at all.

JANUARY 13, 2009

Bill hardly moved today. Lay in bed all day. Didn't say a word. Had only a little soup.

JANUARY 14, 2009

The doctor came by and said that we'll probably continue having these little infections. He is prone to kidney infections. The sore on his hip still isn't cured. He's having a hard time healing—it looks like a hole in his hip. Bill says it hurts. He just wanted to lie down, but they want him to sit up. Guess who won that round. Bill, unsurprisingly.

JANUARY 15, 2009

Today Bill was able to get a good shower, a haircut, and a shave. That made him feel better. We watched some TV. He tires so easily, and he gets mad when I say I have to leave. He wouldn't eat his dinner, so I stayed and fed him—then slipped away. His blood sugar was a little high, and they gave him more insulin—which I don't think he needs, but the doctor is still giving it for now. I will argue that another day. I have appointments all day tomorrow, so I'll be back on Saturday. He did seem better today than in the past month.

JANUARY 17, 2009

When I arrived, we couldn't find Bill. An aide and I started looking and calling. Finally I heard this male voice at the end of one of the halls calling, "Help!" I knew instantly it was Bill, so I opened the door to a room (not his), and there he was upside down on the floor with the chair on top of him—all tied in. Thank God the woman wasn't in her room. He probably would have scared her to death. The aide said, "Don't touch him," and immediately pushed the emergency button. He yelled out in the hall, "Man down in Room 209!" Within eight seconds there were seven workers there with a portable emergency roller table. The main nurse wouldn't let him be moved until she checked everything out. His arms were bleeding, but I knew that was because his skin is so thin on his arms from anhydrous ammonia burns years ago.

The staffers were organized and professional. They put the chair behind him, and two of the aides said, "1! 2! 3! Lift!"

he went right into his chair. They are great. The nurse doctored and bandaged him right there while the others were cleaning up the blood on the floor, and the rest of the mess. He was pronounced "just fine." Just another runaway—though completely disoriented the whole time. He never knew what happened. I don't think he knew me because he called the aide Bebe, even though I was standing right there. Because he wouldn't settle down, they had him on a 15-minute blood-pressure watch for a while. They fed him and put him to sleep.

At 8:30 this evening, I got a call: he'd gotten up and turned the chair over on himself again. This time he had to go to the hospital: they were afraid he had hurt or fractured his hip. They said they would call me from the hospital (it was very cold out). They called and said he was okay. They were taking him back home and putting him to bed. I'm hoping he'll sleep late tomorrow. I'm pretty sure he didn't know me at any time today.

JANUARY 18, 2009

Bill slept nearly all day and was disoriented when awake. He didn't talk at all. He's sore all over. He wouldn't stay put, but mostly he lay around. He's a hard one to handle.

JANUARY 19, 2009

Bill was in his chair all the way down the wrong hall, but he was so happy to see me and knew me instantly. We went back to his room. He'd gotten his food all over him, and his pants needed changing. So I got him all cleaned up and let him just lie down and rest. I played some country music, and he loved that—he kept time with his hands, as if dancing. Finally he dozed off to sleep to the music. I had to wake him for dinner, but he didn't want to go.

They told me he'd fallen asleep again in the lounge. He was trying to get on the couch while still tied up in his chair. Of course, he pulled the whole thing over on top of him. The doctor said he is going to put Bill on some new medicine to keep him a little calmer. His eyes were very glazed over today. His lips are swollen from where he fell on his face, but he's not badly hurt. It's just a day-by-day thing. Bill is completely unpredictable.

JANUARY 20, 2009

Well, he did it again. I got there and couldn't find him anywhere. I was walking down the hall and heard, "Man down!" I looked behind me and he'd fallen right in his doorway with the chair on top of him. I couldn't believe it. I had just been in his room, and he wasn't there. He was so sweet to the aide, saying, "I'm sorry." They were saying, "It's all right, Bill. Just a minute, we have to get the chair off you." He lay still while they checked him all over and gave the all-clear. He was okay.

We just stayed by the nurses' station, where they can observe him, waiting for dinner and laughing together. He said he was tired and didn't feel good. No wonder he's tired. He wheels himself all around the halls.

JANUARY 21, 2009

Bill fell again today. He's bruised all over, but he's feeling better. No changes.

JANUARY 23, 2009

Bill was asleep when I got there. I didn't wake him because I had to go to the airport to meet our daughter Toni. What a surprise! Not only was Toni there, but our oldest granddaughter Taylor as well. What a wonderful surprise. They'd come to see Bill and be with me on my birthday.

JANUARY 24, 2009

We all went to see Bill. He was lost in another person's room, where he'd fallen. With almost no clothes on, he'd gone to the bathroom—a real mess. The aides got him up quickly, whisked him off to the shower, cleaned him up, put clean clothes on, and got him to his room so we could visit. He'd forgotten he had fallen by the time he got to his room.

He had a hard time trying to figure out two Tonis because Toni and her daughter Taylor look so much alike. He was very happy to see them. I think he finally figured out the "real Toni." We really had a good visit, then pushed him to the dining room and slipped away.

JANUARY 25, 2009

We had a busy day with everyone coming to visit Bill. Actually, he's better since Toni has been there. I'm so glad. He even joked a little. I think Toni perked up his spirits.

JANUARY 26, 2009

Today was my birthday, so Toni, Taylor, and I slipped off to Mexico early this morning and had a play day. We celebrated with a wonderful dinner and margaritas at Arturo's. Suzanne took over and went to see Bill. She also thought he seemed better than in a long time.

JANUARY 27, 2009

One of the head nurses whom I love, Sue, called early around 9:30 and said Bill has had the worst fall he has ever had. He didn't break anything, but they're keeping him right by the nurses' station to watch him. We went over, of course, and he didn't remember the fall at all. He was in good spirits and even said it was a good day. We stayed and had a great visit until dinner—he sure looks beat-up. He looks like he lost a bareknuckle fight.

JANUARY 29, 2009

We had another good visit. Bill was contented. When it came time for dinner, I got him in his chair and rolled him all the way to the door of his room. Then he started pushing the chair backward and wanted back in bed. He wouldn't budge. So I put him in the bed and told he nurses. I thought well, they can handle that. I can't. But he does seem better.

JANUARY 30, 2009

Bill doesn't feel good today. They had to put him back to bed at 3:30. He didn't feel like sitting up. Even though there was singing in the dining room, he didn't want to go listen. His eyes were glazed over, but he didn't seem to hurt in any one place. He just didn't feel good. I let the nurse get him up for dinner because he had already told me he did not want to eat today. He said, "I'm scared." He held my hand so tight the whole time. He was wearing someone else's pants—I guess they just grabbed some pants.

FEBRUARY 2, 2009

H.K. Stanfield is one of Bill's dear childhood friends. He and his wife have remained close to us all these years. Anyway, H.K. came in late and was eager to see Bill. I'd gone over earlier, but we went back together. Bill knew him immediately. They really had a good visit. Bill responded as if he knew what they were talking about. H.K. commented to me that Bill seemed completely normal. He was so glad to see that Bill seemed about the same as the previous year when he was here. I just let it go. He is nowhere near where he was last year. But he was having a good day. Also, Bill still knows how to act like he knows things. I've noticed when they talk about old times, Bill will just agree—like he remembers it the same way, but I doubt that he remembers any of it. Anyway, he was very happy to see H.K.

FEBRUARY 4, 2009

Another good day. We watched a Western. He didn't want to go to dinner, but we took him there.

FEBRUARY 5, 2009

Another good day. More Westerns. Ate candy and drank Dr. Pepper. He wound up in the wrong room at one point, but we found him.

Good or Bad:
Thinking Makes It So

Desperately sick with food poisoning, I had to go to the hospital, where they kept me for three days. I felt just terrible. When I went to see Bill today, he hadn't even missed me. I told him I had been very, very sick and he said, "Oh, you should just let me take care of you. I'm glad you are home, though." He thinks I live there with him. I quizzed him a bit and told him I really live in Ingleside. He said, "What's Ingleside?" Finally he said, "Well, I'm just glad we live here and we have so many friends." He really likes Sam—that's his best buddy. They're in the same boat. They don't like their chairs, and they'll talk for hours without making any sense. They meet at the nurses' station. Sam thinks they live in a country club; Bill thinks they live in a motel. He's feeling good. That's what counts.

Someone stole the comforter that Shirley gave him, but she said she had another one she can bring over. He loves the people there. It's home to him. He thinks I go off to cook and clean. He always says, "You look so pretty, and I love you so much." That makes me feel good. He is kind and sweet to everyone.

FEBRUARY 14, 2009

I brought Bill some strawberry shortcake that I've always made on Valentine's Day, with whipped cream. He ate a little and said it made his stomach hurt. I asked him if he remembered my always fixing that for Valentine's. He said, "Oh, yeah." Such a faker. He said he just didn't want any more. Watched another movie and headed for dinner. Of course, he tried to resist.

FEBRUARY 15, 2009

Back to Spohn Hospital for a checkup. Big Vicki took him, and I followed. He was so glad to see me when Vicki brought him in. He can't remember a thing. I really quizzed him today as I knew the doctor would be asking lots of questions. I asked him if he remembered the different houses we've lived in, and of course the only place he remembers is 1911 Van Buren, Amarillo, Texas. When I brought up the ranch house, he said, "Oh, yeah. I remember that house." I asked him what it looked like, and he smiled at me and said, "You know." He asked where we were, and I told him.

He was nice to all the nurses, and when they brought him back to the room, the doctor came in and said, "Well, I removed three large polyps from his esophagus and upper stomach. There is still one very suspicious one that I couldn't get, but I got a piece of it and will have it biopsied." He said he wasn't worried. He said, "Bebe, he has more than enough serious problems to worry about now." We'll just see.

Bill was very tired, as was I. We had both gotten up at five o'clock this morning. I'm going to bed early, and Big Vicki said she'd be taking Bill right home and tucking him in bed.

FEBRUARY 25, 2009

Excellent news. Bill can eat in the regular dining room again. I know that's been one of the reasons he was hating to go eat lately. But now he's back with his friends. It must have really helped getting the polyps removed. He can swallow so much better. He is happy and he just *loves* his friends.

Today he was just sitting in the dining room listening to a couple of the worst guitar players in the world. I can't play the guitar, but a rank beginner could do better than that. Bill loved it. He even got up and danced a little. Everyone clapped. He loved that. Now, believe me, the Bill I know would never have done that. But he was proud of himself, and he loves everyone here.

This new Bill that I'm getting used to is something else. He never did "just love everyone," but again, the main thing is that he is happy and really enjoying himself. It may be hard for me to swallow, but he has been miserable for two-and-a-half years, worrying and knowing that things weren't right. Now, no worries, just contentment and friends. He loves seeing me and always kisses me and tells me he loves me. He'll tell the nurses that his sweetheart is here (as if they cared).

One little lady has a crush on him, and Bill knows it. He just says, "Well, she can't help it." I guess the main thing is that it's so good that he is happy. He's being taken care of. That is what I wanted. I just miss my old Bill. But we can't have it all.

MARCH 4, 2009

There really aren't any changes. Bill's doing great, and he's contented. It's funny, but sometimes I think this is what Bill has wanted forever: peace and contentment. He was never satisfied with his accomplishments—always wanted to do more and get bigger deals. He thinks we live there and go the café every day. Today he said, "Well, they change the menu all the time. Maybe we'll try another café down the street."

When I walked in he was wearing his shirt, socks, shoes, and that was it. He was fully exposed, and it didn't bother him a bit. I said, "Well, Honey, we'd better put some underwear on and some pants." He just said, "Well, okay." It didn't worry him a bit. He was ready to walk out in the hall that way. His health seems better now. I think he's improving.

MARCH 17, 2009

St. Patrick's Day. That was always a big day for us when we lived at the ranch. He has no idea what it means at all, but this past month has been great. He has improved so much, just walking all over and snapping his fingers to music. He's really happy. Sometimes he thinks this is our home, and sometimes he thinks it's a motel.

He can eat real food as long as it isn't hard or tough, but they usually give him softer food, and they have snacks all day. He loves snacks, especially the ice cream he gets in the afternoon, with cookies. It's just like pre-K. He and his friends (he doesn't know one person's name) all enjoy that so much.

He is still so happy when I arrive. Now he opens his arms wide and yells, "It's Bebe!" He doesn't care who sees him, and he'll announce to everyone, "Bebe is here." He is so cute. They all love him. Thank God he's contented. He just loves the old movies. Usually now we watch the Turner Classics in the afternoon. He never did like musicals, and still doesn't.

The other day we were watching a Western, and a girl was riding a horse. Bill said, "Bebe, what is the name of that horse you are riding?" He kept thinking the girl in the movie was me. I said, "That's not me." He laughed and said, "You can't fool me! I remember, and I know you when I see you and I damn sure know you on your horse." He is just so much better health-wise. It's a whole new life for both of us.

MARCH 23, 2009

When Big Vicki took him back to the doctor, everything checked out great. He is now healthy, eating well, and walking all over the place. They really have a hard time keeping up with him. I was waiting for him when they got back from the doctor and he just couldn't believe it. He grabbed me and said, "How did you know where I'd be?" He just kept saying it over and over, just amazed. He was tired from the trip, but happy.

MARCH 29, 2009

I had just gotten in from church when the phone rang. A girl named Jan from the rest home said Bill wanted to speak to me, and she put him on the phone. He said, "Well, where are you? I need you right now!" I asked what was wrong, and he said, "I am sick and you have to be here and you better get here fast." I said, "Okay, I'll hurry."

When I arrived, he was sitting talking to Sam and another man. He saw me and said, "Well, what are you doing here?" He seemed sort of glad to see me, but clearly he wasn't as excited as he sometimes is. Of course, he didn't know he had called. I went to the desk and made it plain to them to *not* give him the phone or make a phone call for him again. If he needed me for anything, they should be the ones calling. I stayed six hours today, and he still had a fit when I left. I had to have a nurse help me slip out.

MARCH 30, 2009

We had a good visit and watched a movie as usual. Bill really fought going to dinner. So I said, "Well, I'll go and ask them if we can eat later." He followed me, just as I knew he would. I walked into the dining room and the girls started talking to him and one said, "Bill, your dinner is ready now." She walked him over to his place. Just put some pretty girls around him, and he will follow.

MARCH 31, 2009

Bill has been clingy all day. We watched a movie. When it was dinnertime, he was glued to me. We walked down the hall, and he was right by me and said, "I am going wherever you go." Then Big Vicki came up and said, "Bill, what are you doing today?" Then she looked at me and said, "Don't you have to go get your shot, Bebe?" She knew I was trying to get away, and so I slipped out.

Shortly after, Vicki was getting off work and also leaving. I looked up from my car and *there was Bill in the street.* I jumped out of the car and ran to him. Meanwhile, Fae, my friend, had seen him slip outside when someone else had opened the door. She yelled for help: "Bill's outside!" They pushed the alarm, and Fae was running toward him just as I was, and we reached Bill about the same time. She calmly asked, "Bill, where are you going?" He looked really confused, and I took his arm and starting walking back to the home with Fae on the other side. Then the aides were there, and one of them said, "Bill, tell me again where you're from." "Amarillo." She said, "Amarillo. Well, did you know the Browns there?" Bill looked so surprised and said, "Yes, Bobby Brown was one of my best friends." She said, "Well, how is Bobby doing?" Then she gave me the signal to run. I did, but sat in the car until I saw that he was safely inside the building again.

I called Fae later, as I knew she was watching it all, and she said there were about four nurses and aides there walking him into the dining room and they were all talking about Amarillo and the Browns. Bill was happy as could be. No more trouble.

What's worrying me is that it seems he is at new stage now—acting more irrational. I must talk to the doctor. He has never tried to go out the door before, and I'm afraid he would have just kept walking. It worries me so much. I get frustrated, and I'm not sure what to do next. I know now that I can't take care of him, and that this is the best place for him. Where else is there?

APRIL 19, 2009

Bill and I watched the OU game, and he was great. I can remember when he used to cuss OU every time they played. But today he loved them. He loves almost everything. I went early and stayed until dinner. After he had a little accident, I changed his clothes. He said, "I like it when you fix me. Sometimes they get mad at me for this." He's just like a little kid. He just doesn't know until it's too late. This did let me know that he knows when they are mad at him about something—so he has a little memory sometimes.

APRIL 20, 2009

Two friends called today to check on Bill. They seem concerned, but said they wouldn't be going to see him (which I would not have let them do anyway) because they want to remember him the way he was—I really don't blame anyone for that. Today Bill had a tummyache, diarrhea, and a cough. Spirit's good, but just all curled up in bed and trying to watch a movie. Sure glad Tye got that TV.

APRIL 21, 2009

Wandering around, Bill had wet his pants. I got him changed and we watched TV. He drank lemonade, and I drank coffee. He is really worried about an underpass—he told me that he doesn't want us going there anymore. I said okay. He then said, "Good. That makes me feel better. You know, that underpass has been nothing but trouble to us." I thought he was doing pretty well, but as soon as I got home a staffer called and said Bill's cough had suddenly gotten much worse within just the last hour. He was now running a fever. They called the doctor who put him on an antibiotic. I knew he hadn't felt good and seemed cold all day.

APRIL 23, 2009

I didn't go yesterday. I had a mammogram (fun), but also I didn't want to catch Bill's cough. Last time he had one I got really sick for three weeks. But I did go today. He still has a cough, and his blood pressure is high—maybe. A new aide took it five times before finally deciding it was 185/50, which makes little sense—it couldn't have been that reading. I'll take my own blood-pressure kit tomorrow and check for myself.

Bill was really cold today. I kept wrapping him in the comforter, and we watched an old Errol Flynn movie and Bill recognized him! Flynn has been dead nearly 50 years, but he recognized him and liked the movie.

Bill was in his room when I got there, and when I walked in he said, "Oh thank God, what are we going to do about all of this?" I asked, "About what?" He said, "Well, you know, they are making all those plans down there and I don't know what will happen to us. Bebe, I was looking for you and then thank God you are here—now do we have a car or anything?" I said, "Yes, we still have a car, so we are okay." He said, "Well, I just talked to someone and we gotta go *now*!" He was talking up a storm and was very nervous. I said, "Well, I just found out—it is all settled and we don't have to worry." He said, "Are you sure?" I said, "Yes, we are okay. The problems are all worked out." He lay back down so relieved and said, "Oh, Bebe, I guess we are really lucky, you know." When he imagines these things it just scares him to death. He just gets terrified.

APRIL 24, 2009

Well, today was karaoke day. Oh Lordy. Betty, the head nurse, was singing. Big Vicki and Bill were all up front with the mics, and Bill was singing "Hound Dog" at the top of his lungs—so animated. He just danced around and waved his hands holding on to his mic—and snapping his fingers to the music. He just had a ball. I just sat there and watched the show. When he finished, they all clapped as he bowed and said "thank you" to the audience. (About half of them were asleep.) When we started to leave, he bowed again and looked back and waved to say, "Thank you, thank you"—just like Elvis. It was simply hilarious, and they just kept clapping.

As we were walking to the room he said, "Do you think I was really good?" and I said, "Oh, yes I do." He said, "You know I can do better. I just need to work on it a little." I said, "Oh, yeah? That would be good." He smiled down at me as we were walking and said, "Well, the crowd really loved it, didn't they?" "Yes, they did." When we got to his room he lay down, completely exhausted. You know it's hard on the stars. But he really enjoyed himself and was really cute standing right there between Betty and Big Vicki—snapping his fingers and keeping the rhythm—not missing a beat. And he was singing well! One woman rolled over to me and said, "He's good—man, he can really sing!" He walked away every bit the star.

APRIL 25, 2009

Today an African-American singer/preacher came by—the one who wants everyone to say "Amen!" all the time. Bill just loved him and hollered "Amen!" whenever the entertainer wanted it. "If you love the Lord, say 'I love the Lord.'" Bill and the ones who were awake would shout, "I love the Lord—Amen!" We were served cake and ice cream and then went back to the room. Bill was really worn out and ready to lie down. I put my feet under his covers and we watched a movie.

APRIL 26, 2009

Bill was asleep when I got there. More musicians were in the dining room, but he wasn't there and didn't want to go. I was surprised, but he was asleep and really tired. Coughing again, and congested. I got him to the bathroom, and changed his Depends, and got him back in bed. He didn't want to move.

APRIL 27, 2009

Bill's cough was really bad today. He's extremely congested, so they've had to step up the medicine. It seems like he lives on antibiotics. The others aren't sick. It's always Bill. He just stays sick more than well. He's so cold.

APRIL 28, 2009

He seemed a little better. They're feeding him in bed. He looks bad.

MAY 1, 2009

He is ready to go to Amarillo. He is back on that jag again. He wants to know just how far it is to Amarillo. He said, "Why don't we just walk out of this joint and go to Amarillo right now?" I said, "Well, Bill, what would we do there?" He looked at me funny and said, "Well, I mean, let's go home to Amarillo." I stayed with him a long time today. He started referring to "that place," and why are we staying here anyway. I hated to leave. It was hard today. He doesn't talk about people like his mother and father so much anymore, or 1911 Van Buren. Now he has no idea where we have ever lived or where he has ever lived. He does seem to have a few grade-school memories.

MAY 2, 2009

Kentucky Derby Day. I made a big deal out of it and took Bill the newspaper with all the Derby horses' names and stats. He was tickled that I was there and could get the races on TV. He would say he's betting on the gray one, then the black one, and finally he said, "That one! That one!" And it was the horse that was the longest shot of all—50 to 1. I'll be damned, but it won. He said, "Yeah, I knew it was a New Mexico horse." He was just as happy as could be, and I had little treats for us with our drinks (Dr. Pepper and coffee). It was certainly different from how it used to be for Kentucky Derby Day. You can bet that if we had won a 50 to 1 shot, it wouldn't have been Dr. Pepper and coffee.

MAY 4, 2009

When I arrived, Bill was wandering. So I started talking to one of the nurses and walked up behind him and hugged him. Then he looked at my face and just grabbed me and hugged me and said, "Oh, you are really here!" We got our drinks and went to watch a movie. He wrapped up in his comforter with my feet to "keep them warm." He said, "Our son was here today and told me a lot of stories." I asked which one. He said, "That one." And pointed to Tye. I asked what his name is and he said, "Tye." That let me know he actually had thoughts today. Amazing. I wasn't sure that Tye had actually been there because he had been away. Bill said they talked on the street. "Well, I'm not sure, but we talked and he had to go do some stuff." I called Tye later, and indeed he had gone to visit his Dad.

MAY 5, 2009

Today is Toni's birthday—the big 50. I told Bill and he said, "Oh yeah, I knew it was her birthday." I asked whether he knew how old she is, and he said, "Well, I should." I said, "Yeah, well, how old is she?" He said, "You can't trick me. Don't you know?" He laughed and talked about her a little as we watched a movie. This was actually a very good day for Toni. She got the job as director at the Chamber of Commerce in Las Vegas. Lucky day for Toni, and lucky day for us that she's our daughter.

MAY 6, 2009

I was telling Bill about Toni's job, and he said, "She will be running Vegas for them pretty soon, and she can do it too." He seemed pretty confident of that. He was feeling good and relaxed—he seems to be remembering some things. This is just flooring me.

MAY 7–9, 2009

Bill is pretty much the same. He's telling me all kinds of stories, none of them making any sense, but it seems a pretty big thing to him. He is visiting his friends all the time and really enjoys that. This one guy said, "Bill, I already have my keg of nails. You'll have to get your own." And Bill looked right at him and said, "I'm ready."

MAY 11, 2009

Missed yesterday. It was Mother's Day, and I had a beautiful dinner at Mitch and Shirley's. She had wonderful fresh Gulf shrimp and pasta salad, fresh fruits, and cobbler. So good. Then we went to the beach for a barbeque that Tye always has for everyone's mother on Mother's Day—the friends that he works with and all. Lots of food and cold beer and it was so very nice by the water. I'm always happy by the water. Loved watching the little kids in the water. They are so precious.

MAY 12, 2009

Bill was sitting in the "restaurant" with his friends when I got there. He just stood up and held out his arms to be and said, "Look who's here." I sat with them and drank coffee. I asked whether he had a good lunch, and he said, "I think so. You know this restaurant is really good. It's my favorite." I said, "Yesterday was Mother's Day and I had a nice time with the kids." He said, "Oh, that's good. I sent flowers to Mother, but couldn't get her on the phone." Then he looked surprised and said, "Oh my gosh, I forgot to send Eula flowers." (Eula is my mother, who is also dead.) "Did you remember to?" "Yes. They all got flowers." Looking concerned, he said, "Well, I tried and tried to get Mother on the phone. I will try again today."

MAY 14, 2009

I had a long visit with the doctor, and it made me feel so much better. He is going to take Bill off that one medication that just keeps him in a purgatory state. He and I agreed to just let the disease progress at its own speed and keep him comfortable. Bill wanders all the time. The doctor said that he was there all day long Wednesday and noticed that Bill goes up and down all the halls as many as five times each before sitting down, but can't find his own room. He doesn't know which hall he lives on. The doctor said he will continue to gradually lose weight, and he will lose his desire to eat and ability to feel hunger. Bill doesn't know now whether he is hungry or not. He said, "I can tell you this. He is definitely in the last stages of Alzheimer's. There is no cure. We will simply take care of him so that he has no pain and is comfortable."

Wish I Knew His Mind

Bill was in bed all wrapped up when I got there. He was so glad to see me. We watched a movie, and I noticed his eyes were swollen and puffy. It must be the kidneys again. I didn't bring it up, but I've noticed that the swelling and puffy eyes always precede the infection. He really didn't want me to go and wouldn't let loose of my hands, so I stayed until he was asleep. I think he thinks that as long as he holds on to me and I am there, he's safe. He can hear a pin drop a mile away and will wake up and say, "What's going on in that street?"

Tomorrow is our grandson Sean's college graduation. I'm going over to help with the party. David and Suzanne are fixing a Cajun shrimp boil for all—there will be a large crowd and good food. It'll be fun. Wouldn't it be nice if Bill could be there? He really quit going places where there are large numbers of people in 2001—the year I had my first knee replacement—but I didn't realize there was any difference then. He just wouldn't go out in crowds anymore.

MAY 16, 2009

Bill was wandering when I got there. I went up behind him and grabbed him and hugged. He put his hands on mine and said, "Bebe?" He turned and smiled, saying, "I knew it was you. I was looking for you, and I couldn't find you anywhere." We got our drinks and went to his room and watched a movie. He wrapped up in his comforter and said, "Stick your feet in." And I did. I said, "Well, what have you been doing?" He said, "Well, this morning me and my friend went to Plainview on some business." I asked, "Who went with you?" He said, "Oh, you know, Old Goofy." He said they didn't stay long and he was glad to be back home.

MAY 17–20, 2009

Nothing much different these days except for Thursday night. Tonight was family night. I went early, shaved him, and dressed him in his pretty white shirt—he has lots of nice shirts, but they don't stay nice for long. This was a new one. I brushed his hair, and we went down to the party. But he didn't want to go. (Same old Bill.) He said, "You know I hate these shindigs." I have been hearing that for 55 years, but he always loves it when he gets there.

We didn't have a good table—the man across from us kept his arms straight up in the air all evening. He does that all day, and it gets on your nerves. He acts like he is catching something. Another man ate with his hands. I have a weak tummy anyway, and it always made me sick to my stomach. But Bill ate his food and seemed to enjoy it, never noticing anything unusual. The music was the worst and the loudest we've had.

After a while, Bill's stomach started hurting and he said, "I want to go home." I quickly agreed and we went to his room. He lay down and seemed to relax. It was past the time when they usually eat: everything was an hour late. He was very tired, so I said, "I'm going to check out the nurse." He said, "Okay." He was dozing off.

MAY 25, 2009

When I walked in today he said, *"I can't believe you found me!"* He just hugged and hugged me. He was sitting with a man he likes, and when we got to the room he said, "I like him but I think he is trying to sell me something and I hate to tell him no." So I just said, "Okay, I'll take it." He looked at me and said, "Do you think that's okay?" I said, "Yes, we can always send it back if we don't like it." He liked my answer.

It was Memorial weekend and I went to the beach with the family. A storm came in—it always does. We've always gone to the beach on Memorial weekend—or had a big picnic at the ranch with all our Groom friends. I miss all that.

MAY 28, 2009

We went back for another colonoscopy. He came through it just fine. We did a lot of waiting. I asked him how many children we have, and he didn't know. I asked him if he knew the names of our children. He didn't. I named them and asked him to repeat the names back to me. He thought and thought and then asked, "Are you one of my children?" I laughed and said, "No, I am your wife!" He laughed and said, "Well, right now, I can't think of anything, but I know the names. I just don't want to talk about it." I said, "Well, where do you live? Give me the address." He smiled just as if he'd hit the jackpot. "1911 Van Buren, Amarillo, Texas." I smiled and agreed, and quit my questions.

He came through the test fine and had only one really large polyp and two small ones that the doctor removed. He didn't want to get in the van without me. Finally I convinced him I would be right behind him.

MAY 30, 2009

Bill was feeling good today—but he had some gas causing stomach pains, and the bed was soaking wet. This happens after they work on him. I stripped his bed, asked them to redo it, and we went to dinner. We watched *The Good, The Bad, and The Ugly*. He knew all the actors before the names came on the screen—he always knows old movie stars—and still loves the old ones. We've made it through another month. Hello June. Half a year gone. Seems like ten years.

JUNE 6, 2009

Bill is holding his own. I really had it out with one of the nurses—one I never liked much anyway. When I walked in, she stopped me at the nurses' station with a smart-alec look on her face. She said, "You know Bill's been a real handful today—he's got an attitude, and I don't like it." I looked right at her and calmly said, "Well, just write it down in his log. We'll see what the doctor says." She wouldn't shut up. She said, "Well, he was in my way and I had a tray full of medications and I said 'Bill, get out of my way.' He said, 'Go take a flying leap.' Then I said, 'Don't talk that way to me, Bill.' And he said, 'Oh, drop dead.'" She looked at me as if expecting me to do something about it. So I said, "Well, if that's the worst thing anyone ever said to you, you've got a lot to learn. Frankly, I'm inclined to feel the same way Bill does."

I just walked away as I had to get something things out of the car. Sure enough, here comes Bill after me as I walked out, sounding off the alarms and the aides were running after him. I turned around and walked him back in. I could tell he was really upset. So I sat him down and talked about stupid things, hoping to calm him down a little, and then asked another nurse for some medication for him to calm down.

Before I went home today I went to the main office to speak with Amy, one of the directors, and told her what had happened and how upset Bill was. She promised to take care of it and said that none of the nurses are to speak to the patients like that. They aren't supposed to say, "Get out of my way." They're trained to redirect them. I told her I had told the nurse to write it down and when Amy checked, sure enough it was not written down. Bill is staying on the same dosages right now. He doesn't remember a thing and thinks we are in Amarillo.

Tye, Suzanne, and their boys all came over to see Bill this week. He told me that he is afraid they will lose custody of their boys. I couldn't figure that out until I found that is what one of the other patients has been talking about all week. It's kind of like the underpass—they all get one thing on their minds and start talking about it. He recognized Charlton Heston in the movie today. Hmmm.

JUNE 8, 2009

I spoke with Amy again today, and she said there had been no more problems. She had spoken to the nurse and told her they would not tolerate that kind of treatment at all. Amy called me again after I got home, so I feel better. I simply will not allow anyone to mistreat Bill.

JUNE 9, 2009

Bill was in the dining room visiting his friends. He was so happy to see me, of course, he just had to tell all of them, "Look who's here!" He was so happy. I see that he enjoys his friends, but it is sad for me. It's just not my Bill. He would never in a million years be contented there—but he is.

JUNE 11, 2009

Lauren, our granddaughter from Las Vegas, is coming to spend the summer with us. He said, "That's nice." When I got home this evening Lauren and her father, Jeff, were already here. They had driven all the way from Vegas in her little bug so she could have her car for the summer. We had a wonderful dove dinner (thanks to Tye for keeping me well supplied), and a good visit. Jeff must catch the early morning plane. So happy to have dear Lauren.

JUNE 13, 2009

Lauren's all settled in. It will be so nice to have someone I love in this big old house with me all summer. She is one of the sweetest girls I have ever known. Lauren and I went to see Bill, and he didn't know who she was. But he was happy to see her, and we all watched a Humphrey Bogart movie—Lauren couldn't believe he knew all the stars. Lauren loves movies as much as Bill. He didn't want us to leave and I had to push Lauren to remind her we had to slip out. She loves sitting with Poppy and watching movies.

JUNE 16, 2009

Bill was entertaining in his room when I arrived today—serving Dr. Peppers and being the real host. Lauren had just filled the refrigerator, and he was emptying it out and passing around the peanut-butter crackers. That's great. We can always refill.

JUNE 18, 2009

Today Bill is totally confused and very restless. We were watching a movie and he thought Lowell Staph (an old friend from Amarillo) was in it and recognized "Harrison Street" (where his grandmother lived). He talked about Amarillo today and wanted to know where I lived. I said we live in Rockport, Texas. I told him several times, and then he would say, "Are we in Amarillo now?" Then, "Where do you live?" And "Do you work here?" He saw things out the window today—things that weren't there. He was very connected with the movie and acted as if it were real. He'd say, "Oh, I remember that. Don't you?" Very confused. He didn't want me to leave. I'm going to ask for another evaluation from the psychiatrist in the fall.

JUNE 21, 2009

Suzanne and Ben went over early because she likes to check and see how much he's eating. He was just finishing lunch. He ate well and loved his cherry cobbler. When she took him to his room, he asked several times who the girl in the picture on the wall was. It was Brittany (Tye's daughter). It was her new graduation picture—very pretty. Finally he said, "Well, she sure is pretty."

He looked at Suzanne and asked her if she know how Suz was doing. Suzanne asked, "Do you mean Toni?" And he said, "Oh, yeah." She said, "Oh, she's doing really well. She has a good job and is quite happy." She said he was so polite to her that she knew he didn't know her. She tried to carry on a conversation, and he would act like he understood everything. Then he asked her again, "How's Suzanne doing?" This time she said, "Just fine." In a little while, he asked, "Where's Beeb?" (He sometimes pronounces it to rhyme with *deed*.) She said, "Oh, Mother's busy. She'll be here later." He just said, "Oh."

When she started to leave, he said, "On no, don't go! Don't go!" But she had to and started pushing little Ben to leave pretty fast. By the time she was at the nurses' desk, the nurse said, "Run! He's right behind you and gaining."

Tye had called earlier from the yacht and told me to take the cellphone and call him so he could wish him a happy Father's Day. They had a good long visit, and Bill called him Tybo (Bill's nickname for Tye). For some reason he seems to know Tye better than anyone besides me. He really enjoyed the visit. Of course, Tye had to do most of the talking, but Bill enjoyed it. Then he would ask who the girl in the picture was again. Later I said, "I heard you had company today—was it a man or woman?" (It was Suzanne, of course.) He said the thought it was a man. I didn't tell Suzanne he hadn't remembered her nice long visit with him.

JUNE 26, 2009

This week has not been unusual except that I can feel Bill getting further and further away. Today we went to his room. He said, "Do you think we've been here before?" He doesn't remember anything, even for ten minutes. He seems contented, and as usual never wants me to leave. So I still have to make a run for it. He seems okay otherwise, eating well and looking healthy.

It has been nine months now since Bill moved into the rest home. He has definitely improved in his behavior (thanks to the therapy), but he's gone downhill mentally and cannot control his bodily functions at all. He doesn't even really know when he needs to go to the bathroom, whether he is hungry, night from day, the time of the year, the day of the week—or anything. I simply don't know what to expect next.

I want to have a meeting with all the doctors at the end of summer—no later than the October anniversary of when all this started. They told me that sometimes when it happens as it did with Bill—losing his mind in basically one night and never regaining any thoughts of that, or of the past—the patients can deteriorate faster than people who gradually experience Alzheimer's. Those people can live at home for years and years and still even go out and be part of a functioning family. Bill has not been able to do that since the night he nearly killed me.

Right now, keeping the bills paid is by far the hardest thing I have ever had to do. We have been fortunate in never really having money problems in our life, but things are tight now—very tight. And I'm still working full-time and closing quite a few loans each month by working early and very late. I have had to borrow money on our farm to help meet the extremely high bills for Bill and keep everything else paid. You're just hit with lots of extras that people don't realize until you start paying the bills.

The main thing I keep in mind is that I want to make sure Bill is well taken care of. For me, that's the bottom line. I do spend extra for him and I plan to continue doing that. I want him to look nice as well as be comfortable.

JUNE 27, 2009

Bill was standing by the nurses' station looking down the hall. I walked up behind him and grabbed him and hugged him and he turned around slowly, saw me, and said, "Oh, Bebe, you make my day! You are my life." We went to the room and he talked and said he'd been talking to some guys from Clarendon, but they weren't right. Then he looked at me and said, "When can I come live with you? I will do anything you want. I just want to be with you all the time. We don't have to live in Amarillo." I felt so sad all the way home. Again, I am trying to figure out if it could be possible to bring him home in a little while.

JUNE 30, 2009

A quiet week. Bill is doing well. I'm wondering how long I can pay. I checked out the possibility of help that would be needed at home. It's significantly more money. I must do a lot of planning. I hope things will work out. At least he is doing well.

JULY 1, 2009

It seems like Bill has been here forever. He is so confused today. Damn, the real Bill could not stand this. But this Bill is completely serene. He told me he had met with a bunch of guys from Clarendon today. But they don't know what to do about "it."

JULY 4, 2009

I went early today while he was still asleep, so I let him sleep. When he woke he was happy to see me and said, "Oh, I'm so glad you're back from Dallas. How was your meeting?" I said, "Fine." He said, "Did you go alone or did you have someone to go with you?" I said, "My friend Jeanette went with me." I added, "You know I don't like Dallas." He said, "Me neither." He said "that bunch" came and he is not sure what they want, but some of them went north and some went south. He was tired today. Lauren and I watched a movie with him and then slipped away.

JULY 10, 2009

I met with our lawyer today. He's going to try to see if he can get me some insurance help on some of the medication. There is something on Medicaid that covers most medicine for Alzheimer's patients. It could save us a lot of money, which would be wonderful. He is helping me with a lot of the papers to be sure everything is up to par.

All weekend we watched movies. Bill slept a lot. I mentioned that we might go on a little vacation with Toni and he said, "No, I don't want to go. You all just go ahead." He had some business to do and just couldn't get away. I am determined to see how he does or can do on the outside. Although I have been told not to take him out by the doctors, I must find out myself.

JULY 14, 2009

We had a good long visit, and Bill definitely doesn't want to go *anywhere*. I am unhappy with the home because they tell me he will not adjust to outside routine. *I have to know.*

JULY 15, 2009

They had the Senior Prom tonight. Lauren and I dressed up fancy, and we dressed Bill up real sharp. I had a beautician do his hair. The hall was decorated beautifully. They really went all-out. When we entered the dining room, a live band was playing all '50s music—much better music than usual. We all three sat down. All the women were dressed to kill, and the home had made sure that each woman had her hair done, a manicure—the works. One man even wore a white dinner jacket to be with his wife (who doesn't know *anything*), but he had her decked out in jewelry and looking beautiful. You can tell he worships her. He is there each day.

Up wheeled a fancy-dressed lady in her chair, right next to me. She leaned over and waved to Bill. Lauren was on one side of him, and I on the other. Then she leaned way over and said, "Hi, Bill!" He said hi back but barely looked at her. Then she looked at me and said, "Isn't he just the sweetest, best-looking thing?" "Yes." Then she said, "Well, how do you know Bill?" When I said, "I'm his wife," she slammed her hands down on the table and said, "Well, hell! I thought you were dead!"

They took pictures of Bill and me dancing and of Bill and Laruen. He danced with all the nurses also. He really had a ball. When he started fading, I started him down the hall and Lauren went to get the nurse to put him to bed. Bill loved the music and the dancing. So did Lauren and I. Lauren will always remember this dance with Poppy.

JULY 16, 2009

Lauren, Bill, and I had a long visit and watched movies. He insists that he doesn't want to go anywhere. When I bring it up, the people at the home say it would be a mistake, that he'll have to readjust to the house, and that he'll be more confused than ever if I take him out. They're trying to teach him to play bingo. He has trouble finding the numbers, but he does pretty well. It's hard for him since he can't read anymore.

I showed him the pictures of the Senior Prom and of us dancing, and he didn't remember a thing. Nothing. They had taken him to a ballgame the night before to try to get him out for an activity, and I asked him about that. He didn't even know he had gone. It was baseball game in Corpus Christi at the new stadium. He can't tell whether he has eaten or not.

I went back as he was leaving the dining room after he had eaten and said, "What did you have for lunch?" He said, "I didn't eat today."

He still doesn't know where his room is, and he can't identify anything in it—although they're all his things that I've brought from home. He still knows his dad's old football picture of him playing at the University of Texas—in 1922. There is one other picture he always knows: one of Bill and me at the ranch in 1956 just after driving the cattle down from the pastures to the main corral at the house. He had told me years ago that he wanted that on our tombstone. He still loves that, and he knows it is me and my horse. But he doesn't seem to know himself.

JULY 21, 2009

Bill had been looking for me everywhere when I arrived. He was so happy to see me, so we watched TV and he was having trouble with a man he didn't like. I never did find out who it was, or whether it was even a real person. He also told me that he had gone to Clarendon this morning. Clarendon is the small town near our ranch where he bought cattle feed and supplies for the ranch.

The Hard Lessons of Port Aransas

JULY 28, 2009

I met with the rest-home people, and I'm not going to get any help when I take Bill out. I seem to have less energy, and I don't feel as if I can really work as hard as I have been much longer. Just so tired all the time. I'm now 76, so I may have to slow down a little. Bill has another admirer—the women just love him (they always have). I had gotten him all new clothes, and he always looks so nice (until he spills his food all the way down the front of his shirt, but I have told them to change him immediately). Anyway, this one lady told me she is in love with Bill.

Well, I'm really geared up for the weekend. I'm taking him out, and Toni is coming in. She and Suzanne will take turns staying with us, and Shirley (our daughter-in-law) is on standby if needed. I think I have it all lined up. I will take him out Thursday afternoon and bring him back on Tuesday morning. We will go to a nice condo (first floor) in Port Aransas—this could bring back memories, as he always loved the island so much. I hope he'll recognize something. I told him we were going on a vacation to the beach. He said, "Well, I can't go because I'm busy."

JULY 31, 2009

Toni and Jeff came in last night and we all had a great dinner. Jeff and Lauren left for Las Vegas early this morning. I'll miss my little sidekick so much. Lauren has been such a pleasure. We can enjoy each other just sitting on the porch and watching the birds.

Toni went grocery-shopping for everything we'll need, and then went and got Bill. They had packed his medications all up with complete instructions. He came along real well and, of course, thought we were going to Amarillo. When we got to the ferry boat (I just knew he would recognize that, but he didn't!), he didn't even know it was Port Aransas. The first thing he said was, "When are we going to get to Laredo?" That floored me—why would he say that? Later, my friend Fae told me that Sam was from Laredo and was always talking about going there.

We rode the beach daily—sometimes twice daily—and it went well. He loved sitting on the patio and watching the seagulls and birds and watching the people going back and forth to the beach. He would sit there a long time if I was sitting with him. I quickly realized I could not leave him for even a second or he would be up looking for me. He started getting restless in the afternoon and wanted to go. He never knew where he was and said he didn't like this place.

We would give him medication right on time. Toni had our schedule, and she had to do it all as I could only sit with Bill or eat with him. And of course there was the changing of his diapers all the time and a continual re-bathing and cleaning him up. It was a full-time thing for both of us just taking care of him and letting things like the laundry and cleaning go. They had warned that he might get more agitated than usual in the afternoon and that we could give him an extra pill if necessary.

I slept with Bill in one room and Toni was in the other. Doors were open. Since we gave him a lot of medication at bedtime, he slept almost all through the night with his arms around me. He wet the bed, me, and everything thoroughly. I would say, "Let's turn over!" He would, but there was no dry spot. He would wake up around 1:00 a.m. and want to go—this happened every night. Although Toni and I tried double diapers—as for a baby—he still was wet, and so was I. He would get up distressed. The second night he woke up and fell. It took Toni and me forever to get him up. He's very heavy—6 feet tall and dead weight. He wasn't hurt, just fell, so Toni and I switched beds, and she quickly changed the sheets. Bill and I got her dry bed. Needless to say, I jumped in the shower every chance I got. It took forever to get him up. He doesn't like taking his medicine, and it's hard getting it down him. Although I know the old "pudding" trick that I have seen them use at the home, we had forgotten pudding. So off Toni went to the store and loaded up on chocolate pudding. Then we could hide the pills in the pudding and he would take it just fine and ask for more. He got more anxious each afternoon, and it was harder to keep him calm.

They told us to keep him awake in the afternoon, or else we would be up all night with him. At the home they let him get up and sit with the nurse at night for about two hours and then go back to bed. So if we didn't want to be up all night, keep him awake! That got really hard, as he would just doze off. So we would do anything to keep him awake: go to the pool, walk to the picnic area, ride the beach, but then the ride would put him to sleep. I tried to keep him outside as much as possible.

Toni fixed all our meals and cleaned up everything each day as fast as she could, trying to stay caught up. She worked really hard. I know I could never have done this without her because Bill would not let me out of his sight. He's walking a lot.

Suzanne, David, and the boys came to relieve Toni, and Suzanne took a tired Toni to the airport to head home to Vegas. Bill loved playing with little Ben—of course, Bill has always loved children. Ben was so good—we just gave him a bowl and a spoon, and he dug in the sand in front of the patio. Bill would watch him for hours. Branch, Suzanne's oldest son, got to enjoy the pool a lot and that entertained him. Both boys were so good. David was good to sit with Bill, giving me a few minutes away. Bill didn't know who David was, but he took to him (and in "real life," Bill was very fond of David). They had many good chats. He kept seeing something off near the beach and describing it to David—and of course David went along with it.

On Tuesday morning, we packed up, and David took the boys and headed back to the farm. As soon as we started packing, Bill said, "Okay, are we heading for Big A?" He happily got in the car and was ready to go. He thought he knew the road and once said, "Are we nearly to Canyon?" (That's 20 miles south of Amarillo, and about 650 miles from where we actually were.)

When we drove up to the home under the covered entrance, he looked at me and said, "You know, Bebe, I think we have been to this motel before." When he got out, he saw the old black-and-white cat waiting by the door. Bill leaned down to pat it when all the nurses came out (Suzanne had called ahead so they were waiting for us). They started hugging him and he was so happy—the first time I had seen him happy since I took him out. I realized that he had been miserable and that it had all been a mistake. Just seeing those familiar faces, even though he doesn't know their names, made him happy. While we were getting his things out and into the room, he just sort of ignored me and Suzanne. He was just loving seeing the nurses.

I realized how wrong I had been and how uncomfortable I had made everyone—probably poor Bill most of all—in that expensive condo. All he wanted the whole time was to "head for Amarillo." Now he is relaxed. The nurse came to me and said, "Why don't you and Suzanne leave quickly—it's almost lunchtime and we'll take him in for lunch by Sam. He can see all his buddies and then we will put him down for a nap. Don't worry, Bebe, we'll take over."

Actually, I did feel relieved, as I was totally exhausted. I am so tired I can hardly move. But I'm pretty happy, and I have a new attitude. I am learning, and sometimes must learn the hard way. This was hardly the best vacation ever. I was able to see Bill's life for 24 hours at a time. Now I know he has to have round-the-clock care. My knees are killing me, and I'm just worn out. So are my two wonderful daughters, and they're young. Lesson learned. Duh.

Meet Nurse Ratched

Bill didn't feel good today. I think he was all worn out from the trip. He was all curled up in the comforter Toni brought him, and he said he didn't feel good at all.

AUGUST 8, 2009

This is our 56th wedding anniversary. He didn't get the connection, so I just dropped it. We watched a movie and relaxed. He seems better today.

AUGUST 9, 2009

Sunday. So we have the weekend staff. I went early so we could visit longer. He was at the nurses' station, and that same damn blonde nurse was telling Bill, loudly, "Go to your room! You are in my way!" She was pointing that finger toward his room. I just stopped to watch as I was behind her and saw her pointing that finger. Bill didn't budge. He turned toward her and said, "You go to hell." I was waiting to see if he would say or do more—and was afraid he would, so I walked right up and he saw me coming and came running to me like a little kid. I turned to the nurse and said, "That isn't going to work. I will not allow what you just did. You write this up on Bill's notes right now. I am complaining about this. It will be against the entire rest home if you ever act like that toward him again."

Meanwhile, Bill was hugging and hugging me and said, "Oh I'm so glad you are here. I'm in trouble—I hate her." I said plenty loud, "Well, I am too, and you're not in trouble." I walked him away from there. As we were walking to the room I said, "Bill, honey, please stay away from her. She isn't here much." But of course I realize he didn't understand a thing I said. Then I just said, "Don't worry about her. I will take care of her." I think he may have understood some of that.

We went to watch a movie, and I went out a couple of times and glared at the nurse, who acted real busy. I am turning in this complaint. I don't like to make trouble, but no one is going to get away with treating Bill mean. She can talk nice and he will do anything she wants him to. She's just a bitch. I hope she'll be looking for a new job soon.

AUGUST 11, 2009

Bill was sitting in the lounge with nurse Sue while she did her bookkeeping, and he was drinking his Dr. Pepper and being quiet, just watching Sue. She is one of the main nurses, and she understands Bill. She is so good to him, and she'll let him stay at her station, or she'll sit with him while she works, and he doesn't bother her, she says. When I came in he said, "How did you find me?" I said, "Well, I thought you would be here." And then he said, "Well, how long did it take you to get here?" I said, "I just got lucky." We went and watched *Ponderosa*.

AUGUST 13, 2009

We watched a movie with Elvis Presley, and Elvis was in a motel. Bill thought we were there. Then it showed a trailer house, and he wanted to know if we were in the trailer house now. Did we buy it? He was really mixed up about what was real and what was not. He's feeling good, but he's totally confused.

AUGUST 15, 2009

Went early. Stayed a long time. But Bill slept all the time.

AUGUST 16, 2009

The priest was there, and Bill had just received communion. Bill loves the priest, and of course the priest is always kind to Bill. When the Baptist preacher comes, Bill says, "I'm Catholic!" That makes me happy.

AUGUST 18, 2009

Bill didn't feel good. His stomach hurt, and he's had a lot of gas. He was up and down, walking around, and he was way down the east hall when I got there. I called the nurse, and she said he hadn't felt good and had had diarrhea all day. She had already given him some extra medicine for his stomach.

Finally, he lay down a little while and would doze off, but when I tried to leave he had a big fit and got mad at the nurse. When she tried to distract him, he was like a little kid pleading, "I want Bebe, please don't leave!" So I couldn't. It's so sad. I stayed until he was completely distracted and slipped out.

I just hate days like this, and she said none of the other patients do that. He just wants me there all the time. Maybe I spoil him a little. What the heck. I've been doing that for years—since August 8, 1953.

AUGUST 23, 2009

I arrived early, and a little band of old people were there playing some terrible music. It was just awful. Bill was enjoying it thoroughly. I sat down and had coffee and listened with him. I thought it would burst my eardrums. Afterward we watched *Ponderosa*, and he said, "Look, Bebe. That is up by Amarillo!" I could hardly get him to go into the room because he didn't think it was "our" room, and he said maybe we weren't supposed to go in. He wanted to go on down the hall because he really thought we were surely in the wrong place. He said he had to pee so I said, "Okay, let's go in the bathroom." He said, "There's a bathroom here?" Then he said,

"Well, you know how we keep moving around, I just can't get used to this new place."

AUGUST 28, 2009

Bill was in the dining room watching the bingo players but refused to play. They had gotten him to play a week or so ago. This time he just sat with his lemonade. He does have a really hard time matching numbers, and usually they are already calling out another number by the time he has found a number. Then he forgets. So this time he declined to do anything. He was happy to see me come in and said, "You can get me out of here. I hate bingo!" He thinks he can't just get up and walk out. I keep telling him to walk out if he doesn't like something. But he can't remember. We got some ice for him to eat, and me some coffee. Inside the room, I found his toothbrushes in the fridge—still hiding stuff.

I went to dinner with Fae (Sam's wife) and some of the other wives. We all had drinks and steak and exchanged ideas and funny stories and consoled each other. I had been feeling about at the end of my rope, so this was good.

AUGUST 29, 2009

Bill talked about the pictures on the wall a lot—especially the one of us in New Orleans. He just kept going back to that picture. He understood it was me, but didn't know himself in the picture. He was quiet today.

SEPTEMBER I, 2009

Both pairs of shoes are gone. He will wear only one kind of moccasins that Tye buys at Walmart for him. I have written *Bralley* all over the sides of his shoes, but no one can find them. I'm sure they are in someone's room or in someone's drawer. They probably don't know it either. I said, "Bill, where are your shoes?" He said, "I don't have any shoes." I will buy some more tomorrow.

We watched a ball game (USC), and he acted like he enjoyed it. In fact, he said he knew the players, just couldn't think of their names. When he was in the dining room, they were trying to get him to play bingo. A little volunteer woman who just loves bingo and gets really excited was trying to help Bill. When she saw me, she said, "Oh, I'm so glad you are here! Bill simply will not put his numbers on the card. He is getting close. I told him he could win and *maybe even blackout!*" As if that is all anyone could ever want in life. I said, "Well, I will help him." I sat down beside Bill.

Earl was the other guy at the table. He's worse than Bill, and has a temper. The lady was all over Earl. They called out O-71, and I said, "Bill do you have it?" because I plainly saw it on his card, and he said, "Yeah." I said, "Well, put the chip on it." Bill said, "I don't want to. You put it there. I told that bitch I hated bingo, and I do. No one can make me play. Bingo is the dumbest thing I have ever seen." Meanwhile Earl was saying, "You know I can add all these numbers up and that is going to be a lot, but what the hell will I do with all these numbers then?" He shook his head and looked at the lady and said, "Lady, you keep your damn numbers. You aren't going to fool me." It nearly broke the poor woman's heart.

Bill wanted to go, and as we were leaving the little lady came running up and said, "Oh Bill, don't you want to stay and play? We are going to have some ice cream and cake." Bill said, "You eat your damn ice cream." We went and had our coffee and ice. I never realized that bingo is such a big deal to some people.

SEPTEMBER 6, 2009

Bill was sitting in the dining room with poor Blind Sam. They were talking construction and starting subdivisions. When he saw me, he jumped up and ran to me. It reminded me of little Ben with Suzanne. Thank God, Andy Griffith was on and he loves that show. He curled up in his comforter and had me put my feet under the covers with him. He loves his new shoes—just doesn't want to wear them—and will not allow them on his feet.

He tried to follow me to the door today, and I looked back and saw his face in the window. I just broke down and cried. I circled back by to see if he was still there and had decided I would go back—but he wasn't there, so one of the aides must have found him. He is happy as long as I am there.

He had an earache today and a sore throat—I hope only allergies. I may have to try some other shoes. Meanwhile, he is keeping the new ones in the fridge.

SEPTEMBER 10, 2009

I can't believe it—they were trying to make Bill play bingo again today. He saw me and ran to the hall and said, "See that nice lady over there?" I said yes. (It was the same little volunteer.) "Keep her away from me! All she wants to do is play bingo!" She really does seem to just love what she does and jumps up and down and claps her hands when someone scores a bingo. She came running out and said, "Bebe, I tried so hard to get Bill to play bingo! He turned his back on the bingo card, and I just don't know what else to do." I said, "Well, I have decided no more bingo for Bill. I think it upsets him." Her poor face just dropped. Then Bill said, "If I see her again I'm going to hide."

He laughed all the way through a TV show called *Everybody Loves Raymond*. I don't think he understood a word, but he just laughed and laughed. He'll watch shows that he would never in a million years have watched before. He told me that he was busy all day getting things straightened out and that he had to tell them how to do it, but they are so stupid they don't know a damn thing about fencing.

SEPTEMBER 12, 2009

Bill was sitting with Earl and his wife—who is scared to death of Earl—having a popcorn party and happy as a lark. When we went to his room, I had brought a lot of surprises. He loved that. I refilled all his Dr. Peppers and peanut-butter trays.

I went to dinner with Fae and the other wives. One wife said she doesn't take drinks for her husband anymore because she thinks the aides drink them, but I don't care if they do. They deserve them, so I take Dr. Peppers by the case. He likes the mini ones. For God's sake, who minds sharing Dr. Peppers?

SEPTEMBER 14, 2009

Bill was socializing when I got there. We watched a movie and I told him it was Mitch's birthday. He said, "Are we the same age?" (Meaning he and Mitch.) I laughed and said, "No. You are Mitch's daddy!" He said, "Oh."

SEPTEMBER 17, 2009

Family night again. (Ugh.) I simply hate these. It started at 6:00 p.m., and Bill has no idea what's happening. I go early and fix him up and have the man come and shave him, put on new clothes, and brush his hair—which always looks pretty— as long as food isn't in it. I said, "Well, let's go to dinner. We are sitting with Sam and Fae—she has us a table." He said, "What are you talking about? I don't want to go anywhere." (That's my Bill Bralley.) Anyway, I said, "Well, it's a nice little dinner and we are all supposed to go. Sam and Fae will join us." Finally, I got him to go.

Meanwhile, Fae had gotten our table. Sam went promptly to sleep and Fae kept trying to wake him up. He would jump and smile and say, "Oh, yeah!" Bill didn't eat much and really didn't enjoy it. God knows I didn't either.

Charlene is a much younger girl whose mother is there—after running a bar for 40 years. Charlene literally grew up in a bar and has the cutest personality. Anyway, Fae and I were sitting there trying to keep Sam and Bill pacified during the program and Charlene came by and dropped off little bottles of Scotch for each of us. She returned with tall glasses of ice and water. Fae and I laughed and grabbed Sam's and Bill's and saw that the other two tables near us were drinking theirs, so we did too. We thought it was so funny, and it sure made the music better.

Finally, Bill wore out; of course, Sam had slept the whole time. So we started getting them to their rooms, but Bill wouldn't let loose tonight. He was suspecting that I was leaving, and he said, "I will go to bed when you go to bed with me." I said, "Okay, I have to talk to the nurse a minute." He went right with me and wouldn't let loose. Of course, the nurse knew what was happening and asked Bill to come help her do something. He looked at me and said, "Stay here!" and left with her. The nurse gave me the look, and I ran. I had just gotten outside and Fae was smoking and talking to some of the others, and I stopped for just a minute to visit with them when Fae said, "Run, Bebe! Here comes Bill!" So I darted to the side in the dark and he was coming out that door. Of course, Fae and all of them greeted him and walked him back as a nurse came running out. It absolutely breaks my heart to leave him like that.

A funny thing happened at the party, though. The cutest little lady came up to me and said, "You know, I just love Bill.

I kiss him good morning every morning. He is so sweet." I said, "Well, that's great. You just keep on doing that because I can't be here to kiss him good morning—so you kiss him for me." She smiled real big and said, "I sure will."

SEPTEMBER 19, 2009

I went early and we watched *Lonesome Dove* again. He loved it, even though he got mixed up about who was who. He tried to tell me what he had done today. He said, "Well, I went to so-and-so's and there was a meeting, but no one could decide anything so I just came home." Then he would start another story and forget what he was saying. I trimmed his hair and eyebrows, and cut his nails, and shaved him. He really looked good.

SEPTEMBER 22, 2009

It's rainy and cold outside. Bill is all curled up in his comforter. It looks like a cold Panhandle winter. There was a scary show on, so I switched and got an Andy Griffith show on, and he was happy. As usual, he had to have a hug and kiss. Then I noticed he had no underwear (apparently he had pulled them off) and his shirt was dirty. We got him naked and bathed, shaved, cleaned, and dressed up nice. He looked like a keeper then. He can sure get himself in a mess. They do watch and wash, dress, and try to keep him looking nice. It's hard.

I did a little memory testing today. I simply cannot give up hope. I quizzed him about the island and the subdivision. He

remembers nothing about the island or us ever living there. I
brought up the KOA Kampground and finally the ranch and
cattle. Nothing. Then I said, "Do you remember us living in
Amarillo?" He doesn't remember "us" living in Amarillo—he
doesn't even remember "us"—but he remembers his Daddy
now and 1911 Van Buren. He said, "Well, I called Mother
today, but she doesn't feel so good." He talks about his mother
a lot and always thinks she is alive, so I just let it go.

As far as people go, I am the only one he remembers con-
sistently. He remembers Tye pretty well also. Tye swears it is
because he drove his Daddy crazy with his shenanigans when
he was little. He doesn't even know the nurse who bathes
and dresses him every day of the week. He never wants me
to leave, and it doesn't matter if it's one hour or five hours or
all day long. Sometimes he thinks I have been in the kitchen
cooking or cleaning the house.

SEPTEMBER 24, 2009

Bill was almost running to me when he saw me, and he
just couldn't let loose. The nurse said, "Thank goodness you're
here. He's been looking and looking for you. I told him you
would be here and found myself hoping that you would show
up." He settled right down as soon as he was with me and
looked right at me and said, "You have to stay two whole days.
Promise?" We watched *Ponderosa*, and he kept ahold of my
hand the whole time.

It was very cold today. I said, "Bill, do you remember us
living at the little house at the ranch and how cold it would

get?" We had some really cold blizzards there. He looked totally blank. So I said, "Do you remember the big white house at the ranch?" He looked like he was sorry and said no. I asked him, "Where do you remember us living?" He said, "1911 Van Buren, Amarillo, Texas." He smiled so proudly and said, "That's our house." Then he said, "You know Jackie Fuqua? He was my best friend, and he lived just down the street." (That is true, and he remembered Jackie and the house perfectly.)

I talked for a long time, and it seems the last memories he may have are from the time he actually lived on Van Buren Street. He lived there until he was 10 years old. He didn't know our children's pictures today at all. His hands were shaking very badly—as if he were having muscle spasms. They turned white and he said he felt "odd." He got very anxious and wouldn't settle down for fear I would leave. I got him all covered and warm, and after a while I told him I had to go downtown for a minute. He said, "No! No!" I said, "I'll be right back." I hate that, but it was getting dark and it is so cold and I know I had better get on the road as it's 26 miles to my house.

I can't understand why the others don't have this problem. They just say bye—see ya' later, and that's it. But thank God the nurses all know they have to help me out, and I am used to having them all say, "Run, Bebe, Run!" They are right there to divert him. Wish I could win the lottery and bring him home with all the nurses. It takes a nurse and an aide with him 24 hours round the clock.

SEPTEMBER 26, 2009

Bill was sitting in the dining room listening to the loudest, worst music played by a preacher and an ex-alcoholic. They both looked like they just got out of jail today. The ex-alcoholic had a fresh cut across his face, dirty clothes, and absolutely worn out boots. But he does have the prettiest deep bass voice, and he really gets with it when they play the music. The preacher is shouting "Amen!" all the time—and all the patients are yelling "Amen!" back at him. Bill just pats the table with his hands and keeps perfect time with them.

Afterward we watched *The Alamo* and then a World War II movie. He said, "Remember this?" Then he wanted to know if we were leaving for Amarillo today, and did we bring enough things. He said, "Will they let us take these pictures, or will they make us leave them?" In a little bit, he said, "Okay, Bebe, let's move it." I'd say, "Well, not now" and change the subject. He kept talking about the pictures and said, "Well, if these really are our pictures, we should get to take them." I picked up the family picture and said, "Yes, they're ours. Now name everyone in this picture." He said okay. Then he said, "That's you." Then I said, "Who's that?" pointing at Tye. "My son." Then I pointed to Mitch, and he said, "My son." Then he said, "My daughter" for both Toni and Suzanne. I said, "Well, do you know their names?" And he said, "Yeah, Bebe." He kept looking and finally said, "Toni Baloney." Then he just laid the picture down and said, "Where's the cat?"

I got his hair all brushed for dinner and had him looking really nice. I walked him to dinner, then said, "Whoops! I forgot something in the room," and slipped away.

OCTOBER 4, 2009

We had a birthday party for Bill today. I had a pretty cake made for him. He didn't feel good, and his stomach hurt, but he was a real sport. Mitch, Shirley, Sean, Bret, Suzanne, David, Branch, and Ben all came, and as usual Ben took his eye all evening. He gets a laugh with Ben every time. He knew Sean immediately and was so glad to see him, and he knew Mitch. By the time we ended, the nurse came by and said, "It's your birthday." He asked, "What day is it?" She said, "October 4th." He said, "No, I was born October 5, 1929." Then I explained that we were having the party early because tomorrow was a workday for everyone, and everyone wanted to be there today. Tye was out on a trip this time, so he missed it.

The home was great. They gave us a private area. I was tired when it was over, so we went to his room. He was soon asleep and I left.

Can you believe Bill is 80 years old? I looked at the pictures on the wall from when we were young, and I can't help thinking, Where did the years go? I wish someone had told me that it would all go this fast. But for the record, I can't complain. The years have been good to us. It has been a year now since Bill has been gone from our home, and he hasn't regained any of his abilities, physically or mentally. He has no idea of time, of course, and doesn't know how long he has been here—or any other place. But I sure do.

OCTOBER 6, 2009

Bill was sitting with Sue while she did the bookwork at her desk. She never minds that. When he saw me, he jumped up like a kid. Then he said, "How did you find me?" I always get tickled when he says that. He seems to feel better. We had our drinks and watched TV.

OCTOBER 8, 2009

Bill was completely immersed in a Western, so we just sat and watched. He had put all the pictures in the fridge, so I replaced those. The door would hardly close, it was so full. Someone found his old shoes. I had *Bralley* written all over them, and he had no idea they were gone. He loves his new gold watch that Mitch gave him for his birthday. This will be the third watch he has had, after losing the "good" one. We have started getting Timexes—but they always have to be gold so that they look real.

The big clock that Suzanne gave him confuses him. He thinks it tells him the TV channels. When it says four o'clock, he will say, "Oh yeah! We are on Channel 4." He lost his razor, but we found it in a sock in the back of his drawer. He had put it in the sock and tied a knot in it. When Earl had another fit, Bill said, "I wish they would just tell that SOB to shut up and act right. I am not going to let him in our house again."

OCTOBER II, 2009

It was pouring rain, and I had gone to church in Port Aransas. So I thought I would go straight to see Bill. I got there and started running through the driving rain and looked up to see Bill standing in the window waving his hands and smiling. When I walked in, he grabbed me and held me. I was soaking wet. He said, "I've been coming to the window 'cause I thought, Bebe will come this way. And sure enough, I saw you coming through the rain!" He was so happy. This makes me think he does have thoughts that no one ever knows about. He may not be able to tie it to something, but something reminded him that I came and went through that door. And he kept looking out the window.

When we went to his room, I wrapped him up in the comforter and we watched Westerns. He said he had tried to call his mother this morning but didn't get her. He said he just wanted to check and see if she needed anything and see how she was feeling. He said he thought she's okay. Maybe he dreamed about calling her. I do wonder whether he dreams.

OCTOBER 13–15, 2009

Both days were about the same. He went to art but refused to draw anything and wouldn't join in. Nothing. Finally, he put his pencil behind his ear and walked out. He has done some nice paintings. He used to be quite good and could draw anything, but he has torn up most of them lately and gotten mad at the paintings. He's now rebelling against any art, just as he did with bingo. He won't even go into the bingo room now.

Forgotten Fisticuffs

Just as I was getting into bed this evening, I got a call from the home. Bill had gotten into a fight with Sam—his very best friend there—who is blind. Poor Sam. But Sam used to be a professional baseball player, and he's still pretty tough even though he is blind and in a wheelchair. They said Bill is bleeding from his arms and Sam got a terrible black eye. I am so upset. I'm afraid they'll throw him out, as they have told me that if he hits the staff, they can overlook it. But they cannot ever overlook it if he attacks or hits another patient. Oh my gosh. I will be there tomorrow, of course. There won't be sleep for Bebe tonight.

Bill doesn't remember a thing about hitting Sam. Thank God Sam doesn't remember anything either. They are having a meeting on Monday to make a decision. They did say, though, that it is not like Bill at all. They have no doubt they can handle him. They said Bill is a "sundowner" and apparently they all knew it but had not actually told me. Suzanne had researched all about sundowners way back. They said, "Well, he starts acting up after 4 p.m., then he is put to bed at 7:30 just like all the patients. But Bill is up again around midnight until they put him back down around 3 in the morning." They told me they had just been letting him sit with them at the nurses' station. Then one nurse said, "We all just love Bill and he's no trouble. We just don't know what set things off." She said Bill had been agitated since dinner last night, and when they asked Sam, he didn't remember a thing. Of course, neither did Bill.

Sam and Bill were right back together today. Oh my gosh! Sam looks terrible. His face is swollen. His eye is all swollen and turning black. Bill is all bandaged. They are both okay. But the staff called Fae, Sam's wife, to see if she wanted to make a complaint. I called Fae and told her I was so sorry and when I saw Sam I could just cry. Fae just laughed and said, "Well, you know Sam and Bill. They both love a good scrap. And don't you worry, Bebe. I will tell them to keep Bill. I love Bill and Sam loves Bill."

OCTOBER 22, 2009

Wow. Sam's whole eye and that side of his face is black and blue, but he doesn't know it. I feel so bad. I felt even worse when I saw Sam and Fae today. Fae just laughed and said, "Get over it, Bebe—Sam doesn't even know it." Fae is one of the sweetest, most understanding people I know. It has truly been a privilege to know and enjoy her. She always brings CDs and her radio for Sam to listen to on the patio where he can hear it really well. He loves it, and plays along with the music on his harmonica. He's quite good. Bill was curled up in bed nearly all day today watching *Ponderosa*. He didn't want me to leave. Finally he said, "You can leave for 30 minutes and that's it. I will not allow you to be gone any longer."

OCTOBER 24, 2009

Bill was asleep when I got there. Fae had told me they had a special party in the cafeteria yesterday for all the people who had a birthday in October. She said, "You should have seen Bill. He sang, danced, and was the typical showman—right up there with Betty and Big Vicki." She said, "Bebe, he was so cute. And Sam played the harmonica." I do wish I had seen that.

When Bill woke up, I said, "Well, I hear you had fun at the party yesterday." He said, "Well, I don't know. I had to work, and you know I don't go to parties. I hate parties." I said, "Well, my friend said she thought she saw you there. Are you sure you didn't go? Everyone said it was fun." He looked right at me (as if I were the crazy one) and said, "Well, Bebe, I would know if I went to a party, and I know how busy I was all day long working on stuff for the meeting." Ahem.

He is really obsessed with the seagulls (always has been), and today he stayed at the window watching them a long time. He looked healthy to me today; I just don't know what to expect next. I want another evaluation from the psychiatrist soon. I want the professional opinion that I am paying so dearly for. When I started to leave, Bill said, "You aren't leaving. You just go tell them right now that you are spending the night here—that I said so." I said okay and slipped right out.

OCTOBER 29, 2009

Bill was sitting in the dining room all alone when I got there, just staring. One of his friends stopped me as I came in the front door and said, "Bill has been going to the window looking for you." It seemed they were kind of irked that I had arrived so soon. Some of the patients are protective of each other, especially the ones who sit with each other at meals. He was so happy to see me and immediately started asking when we were leaving for Amarillo. He wanted to know whether I had talked to his mother today. He said, "She is waiting at 1911 Van Buren." I asked, "Why do you want to go to Amarillo?" He said, "So we will be home!" Today he asked if my husband was here today.

NOVEMBER 1–8, 2009

I have been there every day, and there's virtually no change. It's the same every day. I took more pictures of his mother there, including a large one, and hung them on the wall. He didn't say much at first, but then he said that his mother looks good, doesn't she? It was raining. His stomach hurt much of the day. He talked very little, mostly about his mother. I'm glad I brought the large picture. We have smaller ones, but I think he really loves that big one. It's terribly cold and rainy and getting dark. Bill said he was going with me, and I told him I would see if he could. I told him to wait right there while I asked. . . .

NOVEMBER 10, 2009

Bill was in his room trying to find a bathroom. It's in his room but you have to open the door, and he won't open doors. He was so happy to see me. I shaved him, and we watched a movie . . . and the seagulls. Money is tight, but Bill seems to be doing well here. So I will just keep doing what I'm doing.

NOVEMBER 14, 2009

Bill was sitting with a really sweet lady who had just moved in from San Antonio. Neither one could talk straight. She was talking all about San Antonio, and he was talking about something else. We visited awhile then we walked and watched a movie.

NOVEMBER 15, 2009

Bill really loves that big picture of his mother, and he noted that she's aged a little (the picture was made in 1959). "I think it's because Daddy died. Isn't she sweet looking?" It looks to me like she is glaring, but I guess it's all in how you see someone in your own eyes.

NOVEMBER 22, 2009

I went to see Bill after spending a few days in the hospital myself. I just knew he would have missed me and would be wondering where I'd been. He didn't miss me one minute and thought I had been there the whole time.

NOVEMBER 29, 2009

It has been a few days since I was there for the Thanksgiving dinner, as I haven't been feeling very good. Bill was talking with Sam in the hallway, and it seems like he just never knew I hadn't been there. I stayed all afternoon, shaved him, trimmed his nails, and put all clean clothes on him. I asked him what had been going on. He said he was trying some new stuff, but it isn't going to work and he is just going to quit it. He seems to be feeling bad, coming down with a cold or something.

DECEMBER 3, 2009

Bill isn't well. He's moving slowly and is stopped up—like a cold. He just doesn't feel good. I haven't ever seen him move this slowly. His beard was so long, and it hurt to shave. But we did it slowly. He would get mad at me if it pulled too much. He won't let anyone but me shave him, and he knows he can bawl me out.

I told him that Suzanne had just lost a baby and wasn't pregnant anymore. He said, "Did she cry?" I said, "Yes, she is so sad." Then he said, "Can we buy her a baby?" I said, "No, but maybe she will have another one someday. We will just have to wait and see. I'm going to pray for that." I think Bill is coming down with a cold—he catches everything.

DECEMBER 9, 2009

It was one of the Christmas parties with that loud music. Bill didn't want to go, but we did and sat with Sam and Fae. We were too close to the music, and Sam got mad about the volume. Bill's stomach hurt, then he had a fit when I said it was time to leave. It was really terrible. I had to have the nurse distract him so I could leave. It was so very cold, and I didn't get home until after 9 p.m. The drive seemed longer tonight. It was foggy and cold.

DECEMBER 13, 2009

I had to go to the doctor for my colonoscopy. Everything's fine, but I have a terrible chest cold. I spent the afternoon with Bill. He's sick, too. He has a cough and cold. The only thing he would talk about today was 1911 Van Buren. Otherwise, he has no idea where he has ever lived, his age, or what he has ever done in life.

DECEMBER 17, 2009

It's extremely cold today. Rainy. Just an awful day. I took Sugar with me to see Bill, thinking it might cheer him up. Also, I wanted to see if he remembered her. He really loved her so much. We got there and he was lying down and said, "Oh, what a cute little dog—is that your dog?" I said yes and he wanted to know her name. I said, "Sugar." Sugar knew Bill and ran right up to him and jumped on his bed. He asked me five times what the little dog's name was, and then he said, "I think you should keep her." She lay on the bed with him, and he said, "This is a good dog. Will it wet the bed?" I said no and he said, "Well, then you had sure better keep this dog." He really enjoyed her, so I'll start taking her more often. The home doesn't mind, since they have dogs that live in the rooms with the patients. They take care of them, with a little help, and they have about five nice fat cats that just wander around—feeding themselves under the tables although the home keeps plenty of food out for them. The patients all love the animals.

DECEMBER 22, 2009

Another Christmas party. Bill didn't want to go tonight. I got him all shaved, fresh new clothes, did his hair, and we went. He especially enjoys the little children and the music (ugh). We sat with Sam and Fae, and he seemed to enjoy them. When it came time for me to leave, Betty called Bill up to the mic to help sing songs, and they sang the final Christmas songs. He couldn't resist, and he simply loved it.

Again, the crowd loved Bill. The star had his fans. I watched through the glass. He was so cute and happy. Fae told me he gave his usual stage wave when they led him off to bed.

DECEMBER 24, 2009

Bill was asleep when I got there, and soaking wet. I got him all cleaned and changed and got a TV show on. I said, "I heard there was a blizzard in Amarillo tonight." He said, "Oh, do you think we can keep warm? Do we need anything?" I said, "No, we are okay." Then he said he had gone to Clarendon today—over the railroad tracks by Jericho, with his friends this morning, and they were trying to get things done. But he just didn't know if things were going to work out. He said, "Do you know where Clarendon is?" I said, "Yes." He laughed and said, "Well, I thought you did, but you forget a lot." Hmmm.

DECEMBER 25, 2009

I went to Suzanne's early to watch little Ben and Branch open Christmas presents, then on to see Bill. He was sitting in the dining room drinking lemonade with Sam and his other buddies. As soon as he saw me, he said, "How did you find me?" Then he said, "You know—you just beat all, I never know where you are and think you can't find me. I worry and worry, and then here you are!" We went back and got him shaved and freshened up. We're on the fourth electric razor now. They don't last long here. I just don't know where he takes them or what.

I took the Amarillo book that I had ordered and it shows pictures of the old Amarillo—when he was growing up. I said, "Look what I got you for Christmas," and he looked at it a little bit. Then he got up and put it in the fridge. I said, "Just leave it here on the nightstand." He said, "Oh, no. Someone will steal it." He talked about his mother a lot today and wanted to know if I had gotten a present for her. He kept thinking that the Amarillo blizzard was here and that we were going to freeze. He got really worried, so I told him we were fine and that it looked like the sun would be out pretty soon.

DECEMBER 31, 2009

No New Year's Eve party for the Bralleys this year. It has been a hell of a year. I don't like this getting-old stuff.

Goodbye 2009.

2010

A YEAR OF DIMINISHED SELFHOOD

"What's Wrong with Me—
I Can't Think!"

JANUARY 4, 2010

Well, I sure do have to start remembering never to go on the first Monday of the month again. They celebrate all the people's birthdays for that month. They were really celebrating today. Bill was right up front with Betty and Big Vicki. He had the mic and was singing and dancing up a storm. Then after I got there, Betty started playing "Whiskey River," and Bill grabbed me and we danced in front of everyone. He was having a ball. It was the birthday of a 105-year-old woman who had just had a stroke over Christmas. But she was right there today and dressed to kill. Bill just kept partying until 4 p.m., until he could hardly walk. I got him to his room and he crashed. He was happy and worn out. What a year this last year has been.

JANUARY 7, 2010

Bill was sitting with the bingo group, his arms crossed and refusing to look at the board. But his friend, a one-armed black man he really likes, was trying to play. He was having a hard time putting the numbers on the pad, so Bill would reach over and was most happy to help his friend.

Later we watched TV. He thought we were in the show. He does that a lot, and he got real scared today. He thought we were going to be hurt, so I changed stations. He looked good. It was a good thing I brought another case of Dr. Peppers, as the fridge was empty. I said, "Well, you sure have drunk a lot." And he said, "No, there never were any in it." But his hair brush was in the fridge. I said, "It is just so cold today." He said, "Yes, it was cold when I went to the store this morning."

JANUARY 10, 2010

Sugar and I went to see Bill. He's doing well. He had a little accident while I was there, so I cleaned him up. He enjoyed Sugar. He wanted to know when I got the little dog, and what its name was. Then he said, "You know, we used to have one kind of like this one a long time ago." He said, "Tye came this morning." So I said, "Oh, are you sure it was Tye?" He said, "Well, it sure looked like him and sounded like him." I laughed and said, "Well, then it was Tye." I asked him what Tye had to say and he said, "Well, we just talked about—you know what."

JANUARY 12, 2010

It was so cold today. When I got there, the barber was cutting his hair. I had really jumped on them last week because he needed a haircut, and he would tell them no. I couldn't even comb and brush it to look nice anymore. Margaret told me she told Bill the barber was here, and he said, "I'm not going." She said, "Well, I am going to call Bebe, and she will get mad if your hair isn't cut." Bill said, "Don't call Bebe. I will go." I had to laugh at that. I wish I could have pulled that years ago. I waited and then, when he walked out of the barber's door, he said, "How did you find me?" We hugged and went to his room. I bragged on his hair and told him how nice and handsome he looked.

I can't remember how it came up, but something was said about Mitch. I was telling him that Mitch had been sick with a cold but that he seemed to be better now. Then Bill asked, "Does he still live where he did?" I answered, "Yes." Then he asked whether his mother is still alive. I laughed and said, "Yes, I think so. I am his mother." He looked right at me and said, "You are?" I said yes. Then he asked, "Do you have other children?" I'm sure he wasn't thinking I was his wife. That happens often. He confuses just who I am. He tries so hard to carry on a conversation and he will start to tell me something or what he did and then just say, "Oh shit, it doesn't matter."

JANUARY 17, 2010

Earl was having a fit trying to get in our room. He was yelling and cussing. Bill said, "I'm going to get up and knock the hell out of him. I hate him." I said, "No one likes Earl, but don't ever hit him or they will get mad at you." He asked me where I live, and I told him I live in Ingleside. He said, "Oh, do you have a trailer?" I said, "No. We used to have a horse trailer, but it wore out."

JANUARY 19, 2010

Bill was sitting with the nurses when I got there. He told me his foot hurt. I told the nurse to have the doctor check him for gout.

JANUARY 22, 2010

Toni and Jeff came in from Vegas, and we all went to see Bill. He acted so silly. I don't think he knew what to do, and he can't carry on a conversation. He did silly things like talking to his foot. Then he acted like he was choking himself. He just doesn't know what to do when someone he isn't used to is around. We stayed awhile and went home.

At 8:30 in the evening the home called. They had to bandage Bill's arm. He was trying to shake hands with someone who grabbed him and somehow started that thin skin bleeding. He is okay. That skin is just paper thin. They were going to give him more medication and put him to bed. He won't remember it tomorrow. I really think he knew Toni, but he didn't know Jeff. He was sure trying.

JANUARY 24, 2010

Toni, Jeff, and I went back to see Bill this morning and visited in the dining room. He's much better in the morning. It was a better visit, and he didn't act so silly. He didn't want us to leave, but I told him I had to take them to the airport and would be back in 30 minutes. I have really enjoyed Toni and Jeff so much. I know this was a hard visit for Toni to see such changes in her Daddy.

JANUARY 26, 2010

Today is my birthday: 77 years old. I got there early, and the "musicians" were singing the old-timey songs. Bill was loving that. My friend Lanell was playing the piano. Bill loves them all. They got Sam to play the harmonica, and Bill clapped and clapped and cheered Sam on. They all love it—and this bunch isn't so loud. It's much better than the loud karaoke—and they did all the songs everyone knows—in English. I said, "Bill, it is my birthday." He said, "Oh." I miss those special birthday presents.

FEBRUARY 5, 2010

I have been in San Antonio for a few days taking the new courses that are required for the loan-officer license—and passed. Yay. Suzanne went over nearly every day and said she enjoyed doing it. She kept Bill shaved and kept him stocked with all the treats. When I got home, he didn't even know I had been gone. They had a big Valentine's party, and Bill was King of Hearts with a gold crown and gold robe. He really seemed to enjoy that. They told him that he was to sit with the Queen of Hearts tonight. He wouldn't sit with her unless I sat by his side. So finally they pulled up a chair so I could sit by Bill. He was okay then and let them take pictures. He didn't understand what was going on, but he knew he was special—and he liked that.

They had some *really* bad musicians playing and singing love songs. Bill wouldn't have anything to do with the Queen, so she was kind of disappointed. He was getting tired, and so was I. The weather is terrible, and I was dreading the long drive home tonight. I was to the point where I thought if they played "Down in the Valley" one more time, I would either scream or cut my throat with a dull butcher knife. The crowd loved it.

Today I got a letter saying I was denied the Medicaid help. That's okay. I will make it. I always do. Always have. I know I will manage. I just wish I had a shoulder to cry on sometimes. There are people who are a lot worse off. And I did pass the test. It was a very hard test: only 20% pass. One more to go, and I know I can pass it because I study hard. I am almost first or second in production, so at least I can still keep working and make it financially. I will still get a loan on the Panhandle farm. That will work for now.

FEBRUARY 23, 2010

I took Sugar with me today, and Bill asked, "Whose little dog is that?" I said, "It's mine." He said, "Well, she sure seems like a good one. I think you should keep her. What's her name?" Sugar jumped right up on the bed with him and lay right down beside him. Bill liked that. He said, "Let's keep this one."

FEBRUARY 25, 2010

A nice couple from Wisconsin who are bingo volunteers have taken a special interest in Bill. They just love him. They have really been trying to get Bill to play bingo; this is about the third time I have met them. The man, Dave, gets Bill coffee and will sit with him and visit. When we got back to the room I said, "Well, those are just the nicest people, aren't they? Do you like the man?" He asked, "Who?" I said, "That man, Dave, that has been coming to see you almost every day." He looked at me (with that same look like I am the one that doesn't know anything) and said, "I don't know who the hell you are talking about. It must be some of your friends. You know you are always getting things all mixed up." I went into some detail about the man, and he said, "Well, there are a lot of people down the street, and I simply don't pay attention to them. You know I do my business, and that's that."

MARCH 2, 2010

Sam and Bill were talking and seemed to be really enjoying themselves. We went to his room, and I wanted to just sit down. I didn't feel good today. I'd rushed to Corpus Christi earlier to turn in some loans. I'm tired and mad at the mortgage business. Bill kept saying, "Okay, Bebe, we have to hurry! If we want to get there before dark!" Finally I said, "We aren't going today, the roads are not good." And then in another five minutes he would say, "Are you ready? Where is the car? Do you know how to find the house?" Today I was in a bad mood, so I told him we had already paid for this room for the night and that we were staying here. Then I said I will go tell them to call us early in the morning. I left feeling sorry for myself.

MARCH 11, 2010

I had an appointment with an evaluator girl and three nurses before seeing Bill. I told them to take him off those calorie drinks, but they didn't want to. They said, "We feel it fights infection and keeps him going, and if he is sick, he will be in better condition." I just said, "No. No. No more calorie drinks." Then one of them said, "You bring him all those goodies and they are full of calories." I said, "Yes, those are the calories that I want him to have." I have found out that as long as I am paying the bills, they have to listen to what I say. He doesn't look good or feel good, and he doesn't like those drinks.

MARCH 14, 2010

I went early today. Bill was asleep, so I asked Margaret a question. I trust her more than anyone—I got her and her husband a fantastic home loan, and I think she likes me too. Anyway, I said, "Margaret, shouldn't Bill be awake?" She said, "Bebe, he has felt bad all day and is really congested. We're getting him some medicine." I stayed until after dinner, and Margaret assured me that if he woke up, she would see that he had some soup or something he wanted—but not calorie drinks. She walked me to the door as I was leaving and said, "Don't worry, Bebe. I will watch him and call you if anything happens that you should know."

Our good friend Jim Farrell has died. Jim was Bill's childhood friend. His wife Marlene called me and said the doctor told her the week before that he didn't want to send Jim to the hospital because they would put him in ICU immediately and hook him up to machines. That could last for weeks or months, and he wouldn't be getting any better: he was dying. She does not have a power of attorney or the medical POA as we do. She enlightened me a lot. Jim had been badly sick for two years, and he had suffered so much. He told her he didn't want to go back to the hospital. He had said, "I want to die at home." She was so grateful that the doctor made the decision she wanted, since she really couldn't do anything if he'd said for him to go. So Jim died at home.

MARCH 21, 2010

It's Taylor's birthday—our oldest granddaughter. She lived with us a little while and spent several summers with us. Of course, we just love her to death. Today I walked up behind Bill and put my arms around him and said, "Hi, good looking." He slowly turned around and then just smiled and hugged me and said, "How did you find me?" I said, "I just looked until I found you." He looked at me and said, "Today I wanted to see you so bad, but I thought I was unfindable. You know you just beat all, I just can't believe it." He was shaking his head and laughing all the way to his room, where I gave him a good shave and worked him all over, getting him all spruced up. He sat there as I worked on him and then looked up and asked, "Where are we, Bebe?" I said, "This is our room." He asked, "Did we buy it?" I just said yes. And he said, "Well, I think we did pretty well on this deal. This is keen." He said, "Are we going out tonight or what?" I said, "I thought we might just stay here and enjoy and visit." He asked if it was all right to stay in this room. He has a cough again, and I said, "Bill, you have a cough, and I don't like that one bit." He said, "Well, all right, then."

MARCH 26, 2010

Today Bill's stomach hurt, so I asked the doctor to give him some medicine. (He did.) Bill just felt bad all over. He told me Jackie Fuqua had come by and used his razor and it broke. But he also said he refrained from saying anything about it to Jackie. Then he just lay back down and rested.

MARCH 27, 2010

Karaoke day. Oh my gosh. Bill and I danced until his stomach hurt too badly to continue. He said, "Bebe, we have to go *now*." He was worn out and had to lie down. Frankly, I was worn out too.

MARCH 29, 2010

Today is Sunday, and I went over early. Bill was in the dining room listening to this yelling preacher that I can't stand. I stood by the glass and finally got his attention and motioned for him to come to me. He stood up and right in the middle of the preaching said quite loudly, "Bebe's here!" I was really embarrassed. The preacher looked right at me, and of course Bill was pushing his way through to get to me. I couldn't wait to get him to his room to shave him. We'd have our refreshments.

I've noticed that lately Bill doesn't pick up his feet at all. I mentioned it to one of the nurses, who said she would put it in her notes—with the date (as I later noticed). He can still walk and get around, but he is shuffling and now cannot finish even short sentences. Today he slapped his forehead and said, "Bebe, what's wrong with me—I can't think!" He looked so sad, then he said, "I can't . . . can't—oh hell, forget it." This again tells me that he does have little thoughts now and then, and that he definitely knows something is wrong.

APRIL 3, 2010

I missed three days. I don't like that, but I've been working really hard to close as many loans as I can. The mortgage business is really getting rough, and it's harder to pass loans. The people who buy our loans are turning them back. Bill didn't feel good today, so we just watched TV. At least he didn't have to go to bingo.

Yearning for Mother

My dear brother's birthday. How I wish he were alive. Bill was asleep, so I had coffee and talked with the nurses and relaxed while he slept. When he woke up, he just smiled and held out his hand to me and said, "I don't feel good." He never moved.

He had a different look today. He seems to have gone downhill a little more. He said, "I just feel terrible." He simply never moved. He was soaked through, and I said, "Honey we need to change your clothes. They're really wet." He said, "Can't you do it later? I don't want to move." Finally, he moved a little, so I got him up to change everything. He could barely stand, and I was afraid he would fall. I let him lie back down as quickly as I could. It is so hard to change him. He doesn't know to raise his arms to take the shirt off anymore. We didn't even talk. He just held my hand and closed his eyes, but I could tell he wasn't asleep when he murmured really low, "Back hurts," "Stomach hurts," and "Feel so bad." I don't like that. I am worried. He seems worse to me than he has before. When it was time for me to leave, I told them to bring food to his room and feed him there—just some soup and pudding. Don't want to make him get up.

APRIL 11, 2010

The man from Wisconsin was with Bill when I got there, and he had Bill playing bingo. Bill really hates bingo, but he likes that man. I think he is doing it to be nice to the man. The Wisconsin people are so nice, and they do so much for Bill. They will be going home next week. They only come down for the winter. Although Bill wasn't feeling well, he stayed to visit with them.

APRIL 20, 2010

Bill had just stepped out in the hall and was yelling, "Bebe! Bebe!" The nurses started laughing because I was there. Bill was so excited and said, "Well, I thought if I called you, you could find me—and you heard me! Good!" It was pretty neat getting there just at the right moment.

His hands and fingers are shaking badly, and he can't hold his hand steady. This has happened before, but it seems worse now. He felt bad again today. It seems like he hardly ever feels good anymore. He tries so hard to talk, but he can't get to the end of a sentence. Today he really wanted to tell me something, and finally he smiled and kind of laughed and said, "Oh, well to hell with it."

I got him shaved. That's really a chore, as he doesn't like the razor to touch his face and has little fits. So I got him partially shaved. I have to do it because his skin is so thin and sensitive that it will break out with rosacea if he isn't shaved.

APRIL 29, 2010

Bill was napping, his beard long and thick. I started shaving. Of course it pulled, and he wanted me to quit. It took an hour to shave him. One nurse came in and said, "Bebe, I tried to shave him while you were gone and he said he was going to hit me. So I quit. He won't let anyone touch his face." I said, "Don't worry, I will keep him shaved." Then Bill asked me if I shave all the time. I laughed and said, "Girls only have to shave their legs." He laughed and said, "No, silly, I mean do you shave your face?"

Later he asked me if we were going to stay there tonight. He stood a long time looking at the seagulls, and he'd try to describe them to me. He was really worn out today.

MAY 2, 2010

Bill was standing by the door when he saw me. He said, "God answered my prayer! Thank God you are here!" And I said, "Are you okay?" Bill said, "Well, I don't know what's going on, but I think we are going to have to make a run for it." I got him shaved, and we watched Andy Griffith.

He was just so tired, but he kept asking, "What are we doing? Where is my mother?" Finally I said, "Bill, your mother is dead." He looked at me and asked, "Are you sure?" And I said, "Yes, she had a heart attack." And his eyes got watery and he asked again, "Are you sure? I just talked to her." Then he looked at her picture on the wall and said, "Sweet Mother—see what that man put up for me?" He kept looking at the picture of his mother for quite some time. Maybe I shouldn't have told him, but I was so exhausted today. I didn't have the patience that I should, and poor Bill is exhausted, too.

MAY 4, 2010

Bill was napping but nice and clean. All I had to do was shave him when he woke up. He hates it so much. He asked about his mother again, and he said he talked to her. He said he tried to call her earlier but got the wrong number. (He doesn't have a phone—or access to one.) He said she was okay today. He thinks of her a lot, so I'm just letting it go that way.

I had talked to Tye earlier this morning. He had gotten in from Florida and gone to see Bill this morning, so I asked Bill whether anyone had been to visit him today. He said, "Yes, Jackie Fuqua was by with his wife, and he was talking about something but I didn't get much out of it. I don't know his wife. Do you?" I said, "Yes, I do. She is nice. Did anyone else come by?" Finally I said, "Did Tye come by?" He said, "Oh, the whole bunch was here. Don't know what they want me to do, but I told them I was busy. Count me out." He seemed a little better for a little while, but didn't move much, and when he does he moves very slowly.

MAY 6–13, 2010

Bill is not moving much at all, and he's shaking a lot. But he was talking today and said he had been really busy with those guys and that you know they wanted to do it that way, but he knew it wouldn't work and told them so. Then they all went down and cleared up the other side and it was just a big mess. So he just decided to come on home. Such a story!

I changed all his clothes and shaved him. Then he said, "Well, are we ready to go?" I said, "We can't go yet—they are going to tell us when." He just said okay and lay down.

MAY 16–18, 2010

On the 16th, Bill lay in bed all day and was very quiet. When I returned on the 18th, he seemed *very* disoriented. I changed him again and got him cleaned up. The aide came in while I was changing him and said, "I've changed him five times since breakfast. I'm sure glad you're doing it this time." When I finished, Bill said, "I don't feel like going upstairs." (There are no stairs.) We watched TV, but he seems to be drifting away more and more. He still knows me very well, but doesn't know any of the nurses or anything else *at all*.

MAY 20–27, 2010

All these days were almost the same. Nothing unusual. Bill isn't talking or moving much. Still having a hard time shaving. He still won't let me shave the whole face at once. So usually I get about half the face one day and then the other half the next. He makes me quit. I am going every other day now as the doctor told me to skip a few days. So I'm going four days out of seven unless I feel he is sick.

I met with the evaluation nurse on the 27th, and she said he is doing as well as he can. Duh. He moves *so* slowly, and it's just a shuffle. He seems to still be eating pretty well, and he moves to the nurses' station every day for a while, still getting up in the middle of the night (sundowners do that) to sit with the nurses. He can't carry on a conversation at all. I try so hard and tell him things that are happening with me and the kids and the other people. It all means nothing to him. He will just stare at the walls. But thank God he still knows me and loves my being there.

MAY 30, 2010

Bill was shuffling down the hall and saw me. He was so happy to see me that I thought he would fall reaching for me. When we got to the room, he asked if we could stay there. He looked at the pictures on the wall and said, "Oh yeah, there's my mother!" Then he just lay down and stared at her.

JUNE 3–8, 2010

I can't tell much difference. My hopes are diminishing, and I'm kind of down. My friend Fae says that she thinks Bill is getting worse—that he doesn't seem to see the people that are right in front of him. I bought another new razor. This is supposed to be the best you can buy—the German kind. He hates it.

Today he asked if I had been there before. I said, "Yes." He asked if we would get in trouble if we stayed here and I said, "No, we rent this room and it's okay." He hardly talks anymore, except when he thinks he needs to help push people's chairs and then he'll ask them where. It doesn't matter what they say in response, he pushes them where they don't want to go. He pushed one old man into a closet with brooms and stuff and closed the door. Finally, they heard the poor man beating on the door. He said, "It was Bill! I told him no but he kept pushing! And then he said thank you!"

JUNE 10, 2010

Bill didn't feel good and stayed in bed. He doesn't drink much anymore, even though he desperately needs more liquids. He said, "I don't feel good." I asked, "Where do you hurt or feel bad?" He said, "All over." He just lay there and looked out the window—very quietly.

JUNE 13, 2010

Bill and Sam were deep in conversation—on different subjects. Sam said, "Oh yeah, I was just reading that in the paper." (He is blind.) Nothing made one lick of sense, but they were enjoying each other. Bill saw me and said, "Oh, there's my wife." Sam said, "Oh boy, mine's here too." (She wasn't.) It's hot outside, and his room is hot even with the big fan on.

Anyway, I've been to a psychic who told me to hold Bill's hand and say, "Bill, if you want to go, it's okay." So I did, then he looked at me and said, "Well, if you are ready to go,

I want to go when you go. Where are we going?" I laughed so hard and said, "Well, we aren't ready yet." I guess what works for others doesn't work for Bill Bralley. He said again, "Well, I'm with you. When you go, I go." I thought that was so funny. So much for that. He asked me where I stayed last night and I said, "Well, you know, at our house." He said, "Well, I thought so. I stayed at my house, too." What in the world is he thinking? I surely have no idea.

JUNE 14, 2010

Bill was asleep when I got there, so I unloaded the Dr. Peppers. He woke up, saw me, and asked, "Can we take them with us?" I said yes. Of course we went through the shaving thing, and he's getting much harder to handle. Then he said, "Well, I wanted to move all those telephone poles. You know—the short ones." Me: "Oh yeah." Him: "Well, well, well. You know how they are, so I quit and came on home. Anyhow, I'm tired of telephone poles." Then he asked when we're going. I said, "Not right now." He looked at me funny and asked, "Well when?" I told him I must talk to the doctor to see what he says. He asked, "Why?" I said, "Because they have to check that thing out on your leg (the monitor) that makes the alarm ring." Anyway, he just said, "Oh." It seems to make sense to him.

JUNE 19, 2010

Bill just can't stand the razor. He thinks I am supposed to shave his forehead and doesn't know which end shaves. He tries to get it out of my hand and then will play as if he's touching his face. He still won't open any doors.

Coincidentally Arriving

JUNE 24, 2010

Bill was sitting on the side of his bed when I got there. His eyes were glassy. I got some pictures out for him. He doesn't even know himself in pictures. It's kind of funny: he hasn't been able to recognize himself for quite a while. He always knows me in the pictures, and he always thinks Suzanne is me. I'll say, "I can't be two people in the same picture." He almost always knows Toni, and will call her name—that's it. He does not know his mother's name—only "Mother." He never knows Sel (his stepfather) or Peggy (his only sister).

Lately when I start to leave, he doesn't ask me to stay. I'll say, "I have to go," and he'll say, "Oh." Then I kiss him and walk out. His eyes follow me as I leave. He doesn't ask where I am going or when I'll be back. He has slipped further. He still lights up when I come in and will recognize me clear across the room, just like a little kid. He gets excited, then he'll hug and kiss me.

There's nothing to talk about. He can't think *at all*. I talk about stupid things, and he will just say, "Oh." Nothing else. If I said a tornado blew the house away last night, he would just say, "Oh." He mostly looks out the window or looks at the air vent. When he is up, he will shuffle down the hall. But

[174]

mostly he lies in bed now. He doesn't know when he is hungry or needs to go to the bathroom. He's completely listless.

JUNE 28, 2010

Bill was sitting in the dining room just staring while a preacher blabbed. Two Hispanic boys tried to play guitar. They were quite bad. Bill was excited to see me, and the rest of the time he was completely listless. But he seemed contented—not anxious.

JUNE 29, 2010

Little Ben's birthday. Our youngest grandson. He is a big 4-year-old and is so cute. I told Bill, but he didn't connect at all. He was standing by Sam and talking when I got there. He absolutely refused to let any of the girls shave him, and I can hardly do it anymore. The aide said he really threw a fit when she took him to the shower, and he got mad at her. She is so sweet. Her name is Shanna. I made her house loan, and I really like her. She's working and studying to be an RN one day. Shanna said I'd just have to get some other kind of razor. But I've tried them all.

Hurricane Alex is coming in today in South Texas and Mexico. The rain and wind are terrible, so I will go and stay home until it's over. I was afraid they would have to evacuate the patients, and I'd go with Bill. I had already decided to ask whether I could take him in the pickup with me and follow. I thought that would keep him more settled, and I'm sure he would just think we were going to Amarillo. But we would be going to San Antonio. I will have to stay off the road for a day or two. It's terrible here, and they have all the warnings out advising to stay off the roads. The kids are calling and threatening me if I drive. I can probably get over on Sunday. This is the first hurricane of the season, and the first to come in June since 1957. I checked all the plans for Bill, though, so I would know what to do. They have great evacuations plans, but Sugar, Bill, and I will go in the 4-wheel-drive pickup and just follow the buses to San Antonio. Bill doesn't even know there's a storm brewing.

JULY 4, 2010

Oh dear. They were having another birthday party for some lady, and Bill was at his table with his ice cream and cake. They're just like a little bunch of kids. The fat man with the big oxygen tank on his chair looked at me and said, "I had to save Bill's place 'cause he was late for the party."

Bill didn't even eat his ice cream or cake. And he loves ice cream. He is just not eating much. I took him some licorice today. I've always hated that, and Bill has always loved it. So when I found some on Saturday, I thought I'd get it for him. He tasted it and said, "What's this? Ugh! I don't eat this stuff."

His beard is getting so terrible, and I can't shave him anymore. Neither can anyone else. Now his face is itching, and he doesn't like that.

He had wet his pants at the party. Do I just get there for the accidents? It was rainy and cold, but John Wayne was on so that helped. He never has any idea what the weather is doing although he can see right out the window.

JULY 13, 2010

Bill was very hard to wake up today. We went and got coffee, but he didn't drink his. He said, "I'm glad you're here. I know I'm safe when Bebe is here." He just wanted to lie in bed with his eyes closed. He looked over at me and said, "Bebe, I can't remember a thing, I know I love you. And I want you here all the time. I try, but I can't think." I told him I would always be there.

Today I hired a girl to shave him daily for $10 a shave. She said she can do it and will use cream and a regular razor. But damn if she didn't get scared of him today and *quit*. The very first day. I tried again to shave him a little, but I didn't get very far.

His hands are shaking badly, and he is very listless. He is deteriorating more all the time. I tried to walk him, but he got dizzy. I was afraid he would fall, so I got him back to bed. He never feels good anymore—just seems miserable.

JULY 15, 2010

I got him about half shaved after I finally got him to sit up. He got angry at me so I quit. I knew Suzanne and the boys had been there this morning, so I asked him whether he'd had any visitors. He said, "Don't know. I had to go to town this morning. I had to get stuff settled so things will work out. I got tired and said, 'To hell with it,' and came home." I said, "Well, I thought maybe you saw Suzanne." He never answered. In a little while, he said, "I can't remember where I parked the car." I said, "It's in the driveway." He said, "Oh good!" He doesn't talk much, but once today he asked where we were. I just said, "Oh, you know, the same place." He said, "Oh."

JULY 17, 2010

Bill was standing with the nurses and looked right at me but didn't know me until I kissed his cheek. Then he lit up like a light and smiled and asked, "How did you find me?" He got excited and turned to the nurses and said, "Look, Bebe is here!" As if they would be thrilled to death. He said he has had a busy day. He looked healthier today, but he started fading when I again tried to shave him—which he didn't like at all. He said, "Where's my car? Is it ready to go?" When I said yes, he simply turned and started looking at seagulls.

JULY 22, 2010

Tye had told me he'd gone to see Bill this morning, so when I got there I said, "Have you had company today, or talked to anyone?" He said, "Oh yeah, Fuqua came by and wanted to take my razor to Colorado with him." He was holding his razor at the time and rubbing it on his head. He continued saying, "I told him no, I wasn't going to let him take it because I need my razor and he will just have to get one like everyone else." He never remembered Tye's being there.

JULY 24, 2010

Bill was sitting in the dining room with a fat guy, just staring at nothing. I took a new razor kit with all new stuff and washed his face really well and put the lather on and proceeded to shave. I hadn't gotten one lick in when he hollered, "You're killing me! Quit now!" So I did. I'm running out of razor options.

JULY 25, 2010

I had to call for help to get Earl out of Bill's room. He rolled in with his wheelchair and started giving Bill orders. Then he looked at me and said, "Shut the damn door! But make sure you get out of here." He was really mad. It upset Bill, so I went right down and got help. They got Earl out. He is mean and hateful and just an SOB. Everyone hates him. The nurses can hardly put up with him. I have told Bill over and over to keep his door closed so Earl won't come in. Of course, if he could remember to close the door, he wouldn't be here—dumb me.

Tried another new razor and actually got a pretty good shave. Very hard to do, but it's the best shave I have given Bill in a long time. He was so tired by the time we finished, but he looked good. But then he got really dizzy and his hands started shaking badly. He wears down so quickly, but he looks better healthwise than he has for a few weeks—except for the shaking.

JULY 27, 2010

Bill was right in the middle of all the nurses. They were all very busy and just walked around him as if he weren't even there. One nurse saw me and said, "He doesn't bother us, and he's always so nice to the people in the chairs and helps out when they get all the chairs jammed together." They get in terrible traffic jams with their chairs all the time. Then they get mad at each other and no one can move until someone starts pushing them out of the way of each other. Bill is good at pushing them—maybe not exactly where they want to go, but they sure get pushed. He can tell when there is a jam.

He has a good friend who has no legs at all, not even stumps, and only one arm. Mentally he is very bright, just really badly off physically. He whizzes around in his electric chair all the time, and Bill will look at him and ask, "Where are your legs?" The man always says, "In Houston." He is really nice—his name is Skip. Skip is sharp—just a sad situation.

JULY 29, 2010

Bill was shuffling, probably looking for a room to lie down in. He was happy when he saw me. We went to his room and he got to lie down. He was cold, though it is very hot today—July in South Texas. I got the comforter for him and wrapped him up and he just lay on his side and went to sleep. I stayed a while longer and touched him. I said I had to go and he kind of said okay. He was very dizzy today, and his hands were shaking badly. He can't even hold a glass. He is just worn out. I feel so sorry for him. This is not life. No one in the world would want to live this way. And I know Bill Bralley wouldn't, if he could help it.

AUGUST 3, 2010

Bill was funny today. He was in the dining room and of course when he saw me he said, "Where have you been? How did you find me?" The usual. We went to his room to get drinks and shave. He got quite angry at me so I quit before I had finished shaving him. He just wanted to lie down and pull the covers up and not even try to talk. In a little while, I said, "I have to go." He looked at me and asked, "Will you be right back?" I answered, "Yes, in a little while."

AUGUST 5, 2010

They had a really big bingo game going on today. Skip was the caller, and a dumb-looking aide was the roller. Bill was at his table but shoved the bingo cards to the other side of the table and just sat there. I walked in, got our coffee, and sat down. He said, "You look so pretty." (I didn't.) I said, "Well, I see you are playing bingo today." He said, "No, and there is another line after that—I'm not going to play and no one can make me." I had to laugh: "I don't blame you, I don't like bingo either." Earl kept looking at the numbers and saying, "Don't buy it! Too much money! You can get them down. Watch out! Too much money. Can't you fools see that? They are just trying to sucker you." Finally Bill said, "Okay." People don't pay any attention to anyone else, but some of them are really into bingo and get really mad when someone else wins. Then they call them cheaters. So funny.

AUGUST 8, 2010

Happy Anniversary. It's our 57th. I went to church and Stella took me to a beautiful anniversary brunch at the Omni Hotel in Corpus Christi. Bloody Marys and all. It was so nice. She's a good friend.

I went on to see Bill, and he was peeking out the door when I got there. He didn't recognize me until I was close enough to kiss him. Then he grabbed me and said, "I'm *so* glad you're here! I'm so glad! I'm so scared, Bebe. Did you know I'm going to croak soon?" That took me by surprise, and I said, "No, you aren't." He had three shirts on and looked terrible. I got him to the room and took off the dirty shirts and cleaned him up. I stocked the Dr. Peppers and tried shaving him. I got him looking pretty good, then went to the lobby and got the aide to take an anniversary picture of us with my 10-cent camera. Most of our years have been great. It's these damn sunset years.

When we got back to the room, Bill asked, "Can we go in there?" I started to sit down, but I realized there was no cushion in the recliner. Apparently, he had carried it off somewhere. So I just wadded up a quilt and sat on that. I got an old Bob Hope show on TV. It had a bear in it, and Bill thought the bear was a girl. He laughed and laughed. Then he said his stomach hurt and he was tired. His eyes looked bad today. He's not feeling good. But I can't figure out why.

I asked, "Do you remember where we got married?" He said no. I said, "Silverton, Texas." Then he smiled and said, "Yeah." Then I said, "Do you know how long we have been married?" He smiled and said, "Four times." I had to laugh. When I had to leave, he said, "I love you. You promise to be back?" Of course, I always say I will. He just turned his back on Bob Hope after the bear left. I was there at exactly 4:00 p.m.: that was the time we were married 57 years ago— only one time. It was hot then, and it is hot now. Time sure changes things. Bob Wills was right in his song: "Time Changes Everything."

Fragmentary Glimpses

I left to go to Groom, Pampa, Silverton, and Amarillo—the great Panhandle of Texas—on the 11th and returned on the 19th. It was a quick trip, but I had business that had to be done in Pampa and Silverton. Suzanne saw Bill every day while I was gone.

I drove all the way from Silverton straight back to the coast because I wanted to see Bill. Suzanne had told me that he had been fine, and indeed he looked good. Martin, one of the workers at the home, had been shaving him. I said, "Well, I have been to Amarillo." Bill said, "I was there this morning, and we must have missed each other." Then he started telling me all kinds of things that made no sense at all. He can't finish a sentence.

I have been over four times since getting home, and things are seeming about the same. He didn't miss me one bit. I do know he is feeling better. He says he is always cold, and his hand shakes nearly all the time. I don't know why, and I haven't gotten an answer from the doctor. He is cold even though it's really hot. He always wants to wrap up in that comforter. But he seems happy even though he doesn't know where he is or who anyone is. He seems happy.

Tye had been there with his son, Tyler, and I asked him about it. He said yes and pointed to Tye's picture with Tyler. I took a new picture of his home at 2200 Hughes in Amarillo while I was there to see if he remembered it. He said, "Well, maybe we lived there one time." He spent all his junior-high and high-school years there.

AUGUST 26, 2010

It was so hot, and my electricity went off. When I called the power company, they said I hadn't paid the bill. I was so mad. It is so hot. I got the electricity back on and went to see Bill. I asked him if he had had any company. (Linda Stanfield, his dear friend H.K.'s daughter, had been there.) He answered, "No, I've been gone all day on business." He just turned over and wrapped up in his comforter. It is probably 110 degrees, but he said he was cold. Doing fine otherwise.

SEPTEMBER 2, 2010

Bill was asleep when I got there and when he woke up he was so surprised to see me. We watched Andy Griffith. He loves that. He kept trying to tell me something using his hands a lot. He'd say, "I had to go, you know, over there, and they didn't do anything. I tried to tell the . . . ." Finally he said, "To hell with it, and I came on back home." He was in good spirits, and Martin had him well-shaven.

SEPTEMBER 7, 2010

Bill was shuffling down the hall quite slowly when he saw me. He greeted me with, "How did you find me?" That always makes me laugh. And when I laugh, he laughs. His face is broken out, so I'll speak to them again about that. There was a terrible storm last night, but he didn't know.

SEPTEMBER 12, 2010

Bill was standing in the middle of his room pointing at the A/C vent, just staring. Today he seemed way out of it, and he pointed to the pictures on the wall. When I pointed to his mother, he said, "That's you." I said, "No, that's your mother." I showed him the house at 2200 Hughes in Amarillo again, and he didn't know it at all. Then I showed him the address on the back, and he laughed and said, "Well, if I had seen the back I would have known." I said, "This is where you lived with your Mother and Daddy, and sister Peggy." He just looked at me with a completely blank stare. I asked him a lot more questions about his family. I thought he *might* remember something—but nothing. His head is just empty. He does think the people in the pictures are real sometimes, and that worries him.

Today he asked if we had ever been in this room before. When I said I had to go, he just said okay. I wish I had a better idea of what stage of Alzheimer's he is in—not that it would be of use to anyone. But it seems to me he is slipping away faster than some. I know he has gone downhill faster than some people who have had this disease much longer.

SEPTEMBER 14, 2010

Bill isn't moving much. He's very slow. He seems to be in a daze, but he's healthy and happy to see me. I can tell he wants to talk about something, but he can't. No thoughts. There is no way to talk. It's just terrible.

SEPTEMBER 21, 2010

I had surgery on the inside of my top lip last week. It turned out to be more than I anticipated. But I'm doing fine now. Suzanne stayed with Bill the first night. I guess I was out of it. I have a lot of stitches, and it's very sore and swollen, but not as much as they said it would be. I'm not supposed to get out for a while. It's raining cats and dogs, so I can't go anywhere anyway.

Today is the first day I got to visit Bill. He was just standing in his room looking out the window when I walked in. He said, "Oh, Bebe, I'm so glad it's you," and he sat down. We watched TV. I told him about my surgery and showed him my swollen lip—still very swollen. He said, "Oh." He doesn't even get the connection of what I am talking about, and he can see the swollen lip. Also, it has been raining for five days, and we now have had over 12 inches. That's all anyone is talking about. I said, "Isn't the rain just terrible?" He looked at me and said, "Has it been raining?" He was looking right out the window as it was pouring down.

The nurses said he still sits with them at night, although he can hardly make it up to the nurses' station. Martin is keeping him shaved. He needed to pee, so I said, "Here's the bathroom. You can use your own bathroom." He looked at me and said, "Not mine—but I'm going to use it."

OCTOBER 3, 2010

I saw Bill in the dining room. Before he spotted me, I went ahead and stocked up his fridge with Dr. Peppers and peanut-butter crackers. Then I went down to the dining room. I was shocked: he was in a wheelchair, sitting there happy as could be using his fingers like he was playing a piano. I turned and rushed to the nurses' station and asked if Bill was okay and what had happened. Was he hurt? The nurse said no, she had no idea why he was in a wheelchair. He's fine. She went back with me. He had gotten a little crippled lady's chair when she stood up to reach for something and he wouldn't give it back. She said, "He got my chair and won't get it back! I am holding on to the table and about to fall!" I said, "Bill, let's move over here." He said, "Okay," and started rolling over. She is yelling, "It's my chair!" Then I said, "No, the chair belongs to her. She is going to fall. Give it back!" Finally, he got up and gave her the chair. As he moved, he was keeping time to the music, swaying and dancing.

I stayed pretty long and then went to dinner with Fae and some people from Victoria. We had a great time, and it was most relaxing. Just as I walked in into my house, the phone rang. They said Bill had gotten dizzy and fallen, just missing hitting his head on the edge of the table. An aide had grabbed him, and he fell on top of her. She actually suffered a pretty bad fall and had to be sent home. He scraped his head a little, and they doctored it. He is dizzy a lot.

OCTOBER 5, 2010

Bill's birthday: he is 81 today and looks good. Tye, Suzanne, Ben, and I took him sandwiches, cake, Dr. Peppers, and candy. Oh yes, Ben brought a rock for Poppy. Bill didn't quite understand what it was all about. He thinks he is maybe 55. He couldn't call any of us by name today, but this was not the regular routine. We used the conference room, and it was nice. He was soon ready for a nap. The others left, and I took him to his room. He fell asleep quickly all wrapped up in his comforter.

Martin had shaved him and trimmed his hair. They had dressed him nicely for his birthday. He seems contented and just doesn't know what the hell is going on. And doesn't care. I guess that works okay. We took pictures and got some good ones of him with the kids.

I was tired today, so I came on home and went on to Branch's football game. It was a good one. Wish Bill could have seen that. He loved to see the kids in sports. It was the same stadium where we had watched our older grandson, Brett, play just a few years ago. He had enjoyed that so much. This has all happened so quickly.

OCTOBER 12, 2010

I got Bill neatly dressed, with a new shirt. Martin had shaved him and fixed his hair. I had a professional photographer come and take our picture together. She took it outside by some pretty palm trees. Bill did really well, but he said it was too hot and could we go in now. It doesn't take much to wear him down. I had gotten there early to watch him eat, as I wanted to see how much he is eating. He laid his head down on the table twice while eating. I don't know whether he was just tired or what, but he saw me and then pepped up. I sure hope the pictures are good. I want to send some for Christmas. The nurses all bragged on him again saying how he is always so sweet. Some of the patients are really mean and hateful. His shoulder has been hurting. I think it's arthritis. He was sure ready for bed.

OCTOBER 17, 2010

Two years ago today is when it all began. I call it the day Bill lost his mind. Can't believe it has been two years. I haven't gotten anything done to make things better. At least Bill is being taken care of, and I thank God for that every day. Now I know I could not have taken care of Bill. Me? I'm hanging in there and paying the bills (never easy). The economy is terrible and not getting any better. Everything is so uncertain.

I have been kind of down in the dumps today—just thinking about all that's happened. Poor Bill doesn't remember a thing or know where he is. He woke up happy to see me—completely soaked—and of course the bed was soaked also. I couldn't lift him and had to call in the aides to clean up the whole thing.

Although it has been two years since he lost it all, I now think he has had Alzheimer's for four years at least. In other words, I think he was going into it in 2005. I am remembering more things and remember some weird things happening in 2006. He was "seeing things" then. And he was getting lost. Lots of things happened that I just didn't pick up on. Then, in 2007, it really started showing. He even said, "Something is wrong with me." He said that not just to me, but to Suzanne also in a very serious talk one time. So he knew things were not right. He had started hiding things, but we thought they were just misplaced. By 2008 I should have known for sure, especially when the doctor put him on the Alzheimer's medication. Maybe I didn't want to know or accept that something was really wrong with our little world. In my mind, he was just having "memory problems."

Anyway, now I accept that Bill will be getting a little worse for the rest of his life. And I will just live my time out, and that's it. Again, it's not what you plan. But it's what you get that you have to live with. So handle it.

OCTOBER 19, 2010

Bill was in the dining room with his lemonade just looking out the window. I slipped in and got some coffee and sat beside him. He was so surprised and happy. He just kept looking out the window and said, "Look, there's an arm waving out the window." I looked and sure enough there would be an arm. The arm would go back and forth. I told him it must be someone in a chair talking and using his arm while talking. He said, "I think the arm is crazy."

OCTOBER 20, 2010

Bill was asleep, but I immediately saw that his face was all broken out with rosacea. I went and talked with one of the head nurses. She said she would order some medicine from the doctor. She also told me they'd probably do the two-year evaluation tomorrow and later this week we should have the results. She said he is definitely in the last stages of Alzheimer's, but that he is physically strong. That will give him more time.

OCTOBER 23, 2010

Bill was in the hall talking to Sam—on different subjects, of course. We just visited, and I did his nails today. Martin had shaved him—thank goodness that is settled.

OCTOBER 26, 2010

Family night. I think I hate these nights more than anything. I was really tired today, had worked all day, and my bad knee is killing me—it's been hurting all day long. I realize I will have to have that knee operated on eventually. It went flat out on me today and hurt so badly. Thank God for aspirin—I live on that stuff. My Grandma Joiner took several aspirins every day and lived to be 94.

Anyway, we went to family night, got there early, and got Bill all dressed up. Fae had gotten a table for the four of us, and she brought a little Scotch along. This time I was ready for it and didn't give it a second thought. Bill couldn't understand what was going on, so I said, "We're meeting Sam and Fae." Now Sam is his best friend. They meet every day. But Bill just looked at me blankly and asked, "Who are Sam and Fae?"

When we got to the dining room, Fae had a table, and there was a huge crowd. I know some people just come for the dinner and don't come much at other times to visit. A lot of them I've never seen. There used to be four couples among us eating together, but the others have died. And *no one comes back* after their loved one is gone. It's a memory you want to forget.

Sam had already eaten at five, so of course he wasn't hungry. Bill barely ate anything—even his chocolate cake. He started getting really anxious and kept saying something he had heard Clint Eastwood say in a movie over and over and over. Then he wanted to know if we were paid up. He started getting too restless and was tired, so I said I would go and get the car and for him to wait there. I went and told the nurse, "Bill's ready for bed." It was a tiring evening, and I was glad Fae had brought the Scotch. I really love her. She always looks after Bill when I'm not there, and I do the same for Sam. She's a great person.

OCTOBER 29, 2010

They were having a celebration for all the October birthdays. Betty was singing, and the dining room was full. Bill was just sitting there, his eyes glazed over—kind of staring. When he looked up and saw me he just beamed. Then Betty said, "We are winding up the party—how about doing 'Hound Dog' for Bill and Bebe?" She put it on and started singing. Bill and I got up and danced. He was so cute but much, much slower than the last time he tried to dance. We just shuffled. I could tell he was tired, and it was only 4:30. I was tired also, and my knee was hurting. I really didn't think I could dance. But then how many more times will I have the chance to dance with Bill? It makes him so happy. Everyone clapped, and Bill loved that.

We went back to his room, and Bill took his fist, hit himself on the head, and exclaimed, "I can't think!" I could tell he was very agitated—that has to be so terrible to have that feeling. He knows something is wrong, but *what?* His eyes didn't look good at all, he lay down, then was right back up. I could tell he was just anxious. He couldn't settle down. I said, "Bill, let's walk a little." He agreed and we started down the hall. He stopped suddenly and said, "Stop, Bebe! There is water all over the road! Get us out quick." So I said, "We can go back this way." We turned and went back to the room and closed the door. He really was nervous then and said, "Thank goodness!" He lay down like he was totally exhausted. He didn't want me to leave today, and I hated to because he was feeling insecure, so I ordered dinner in for him. We stayed together he until he was fed and dozing off. He doesn't look good.

OCTOBER 30, 2010

Bill was much calmer today and seemed to feel better. He tried to watch TV, but he couldn't understand the story or what anything was. He didn't talk much at all, but he seems better the last few days. Well, we are starting our third year here. Now they tell me he has had Alzheimer's for at least five years. So many thoughts come back when you really start trying to remember back before he showed signs of the illness. I just didn't recognize it. Maybe if I had caught it earlier, something could have been done. I just don't know. Of course, I never in my life would have thought Bill could be dangerous to me. There had to be symptoms, but I didn't see them. It surely has been a long two years, and I think there will be a lot more years ahead. It just breaks my heart to see Bill live this way and to know it cannot get better.

NOVEMBER 2, 2010

Bill slept the entire visit. I just relaxed and watched TV. That's sometimes good for me to get my mind off the loan business.

NOVEMBER 3, 2010

Bill didn't feel good today, but he was in good spirits and laughed a lot. I told him about little Ben wanting acorns again and he laughed and laughed. He just lay around. Amy, the nurse, came by and told me the evaluation is tomorrow. I'm very anxious to hear the results.

NOVEMBER 9, 2010

Bill was in great spirits today. *Cheers* was on TV, and he laughed a lot. I got the evaluation results, and it's about what I thought it would be: no memory at all. The doctor simply cannot believe Bill still knows me. In fact, he wanted to "prove it." So he had several people go in the room while the doctor was there, and then I was to go in with two or three other people (and say nothing, of course, and stand back). He wanted to see if there was any recognition. The psychiatrist feels that he doesn't really know me. That I tell him who I am. That isn't true. The nurses know that he really knows me because he will yell out when I walk in. Anyway, Bill knew me right off.

The doctor said Bill cannot ever regain memory. No surprise. He's in the very final stages of Alzheimer's but his health is otherwise fair. The shuffle is normal for the stage he is in. The main thing is that he is contented. He will get worse—he cannot get better. The doctor went on to describe how things will be. I didn't like hearing that. I've heard it, I've read it, and I already know that.

NOVEMBER 16, 2010

I've been over every day except the 13th. I had to take a real-estate course for keeping my broker's license current. My knee is hurting so badly that I just came home and propped my knee on a pillow with heat.

NOVEMBER 19, 2010

I went over early today so we could have a long visit. When I got there, Bill was standing in the hall looking strange. As I got closer I could smell something. Then I got closer and saw he had potty all over his arms, hands, and clothes. I headed him to his room and called an aide. It was terrible in the room, especially the bathroom. There was potty all over the walls, sink, and commode, and the commode was full. It was awful. She called for more help and I got out. Two of them started stripping Bill down and taking him to the shower. Two others came and started on the room. One of the aides said it was the worst mess she had ever seen. Poor Bill never knew what was going on.

No one knows what happened. Usually the bathroom door is closed, and Bill will not go in there as he doesn't open doors. They simply cannot watch him every minute. But they sure take good care of things and clean and sterilize immediately. Taking care of Bill requires a lot of physical work as well as just the dressing and changing. It sometimes takes strength, too. Often they must call in the men to help with him. They always clean that room so thoroughly and sanitize everything. I have to stay outside, as my stomach gets upset real easy.

I wanted to stay and make sure he was okay. I went out to get some air, and Fae was outside smoking with Sam and asked if everything was okay. I was a little pale. I told her what happened and said my stomach was getting upset. She said, "Well, after you go back and check on Bill, come on out and we'll go get a drink and visit. That will settle your tummy." It did, and she insisted I stay with her for dinner. It really did help.

NOVEMBER 21, 2010

Bill was lying in bed watching a Western and loving it. He hugged me but never talked. He would laugh at the movie. He seemed happy. He has always loved movies. We watched for a while and then I slipped out when it was his dinner time.

NOVEMBER 23, 2010

Bill was propped up in bed watching Andy Griffith. He loves that. I asked him if he remembered the best Thanksgiving we ever had. He tried to think and then I said, "Well, I think the ones at the ranch were the best with Mama, Daddy, and Tom and all the kids." He smiled and said, "Yeah. Me too." Of course, he didn't remember. There was singing today, but he didn't want to go hear it. He just lay in bed. I asked him, "Are you sure you don't want to go hear the music?" He shook his head no and pulled up the covers.

NOVEMBER 26, 2010

Bill was sitting at his place at the table where he eats. All by himself. Completely at the other end on the opposite side was a woman who eats there also. They were both just staring into space. There were maybe 15 people in the room, but there was no conversation. Everyone was just sitting and staring. I walked up to Bill and touched him. He recognized me then and hugged me tightly. He said, "How did you find me here?" Of course, I said, "I was looking for you and wasn't going to stop until I found you." He held onto me and said, "I'm so glad you found me."

I got our coffee, and we went to his room. He always follows me when I get him up and start walking. When we got the door of the room, Bill asked, "Do you know where we are?" I assured him I did. We were in our room. Then he asked again, "Are you sure it is okay?" I said, "Yes, we have it rented, everything in this room is ours." He said, "Good! You did good!" He went straight to his bed and lay down. A football game was on, and he liked that. It was Auburn vs. Alabama. He never knew what was going on. He dozed off, and I slipped off at his dinner time.

NOVEMBER 28, 2010

That loud preacher was there just yelling away when I got there. I stood by the glass windows trying to get Bill's attention, but he never looks anywhere now except straight ahead. He just stares. Finally, I asked a nurse to go in and get him for me. I was not going to sit and listen to that yelling preacher.

Bill asked her if it was all right to leave, and she told him yes. He thinks he has to stay where they tell him or sit wherever they take him. If you say, "Stay here in this chair," he will now.

He was happy to see me. We watched a TV show. He was in a good mood, and all the Thanksgiving decorations were up. I asked him if he knew it was nearly Thanksgiving time—and nearly December. He just smiled and said, "I guess so."

He loves to pet the cats and always stops to pet them. The big old dog he loved so much died—he always wants to pet any animals that he sees. Charlene brought all three of her dogs and showed them to Bill. He just loved that and just kept petting them. He loves it when the big yellow cat gets up on his bed.

NOVEMBER 29, 2010

I could hear music when I came through the front door. *So darned loud!* They were all in the dining room. Bill was listening, and when I came in he got up and came shuffling to meet me. We sat and listened to the horrible music until he had an accident. So I said, "Bill, we have to go to the room and change you." He looked at me like he didn't know what I was talking about. I called for an aide as we went down the hall.

I had worn a pair of Suzanne's old tennis shoes, and they really did look scruffy. When I propped my feet up Bill looked down at the shoes and lifted my foot and said, "We have to get you some new shoes. We can afford them. These look awful." He just kept looking at them and saying, "Just awful." That's funny because he never even knows if he is wearing shoes and he wears dirty clothes as long as he can—things he never would have before. He always comments on my clothes, especially my earrings. He will say, "You look pretty," or, "I like that." He especially likes me in pink, which I wear a lot. The one day I forgot to wear earrings, and he actually noticed! Well, I sure won't wear Suzanne's old shoes again. He had band aids all over him. He bleeds easily, so he stays skinned up.

NOVEMBER 29, 2010

I had to go to the doctor again about my knee. When I got home, the Wisconsin people called and said they just wanted to give me a rundown on Bill to keep me informed. They went on to tell me all about Bill. This is the same man that tried to get him to play bingo. Now he's giving me all this advice as if I am never there. I know they have good intentions, and they're nice to sit and have coffee with him.

DECEMBER 2, 2010

Bill is doing great—watching TV. But he is starting to get irritated around 3:00 in the afternoon instead of 4:00. I suggested to the nurses that they give him the medication a little earlier. Of course, he's still getting up at midnight.

DECEMBER 5, 2010

We've been having fusses over the shaving again. The electric razor won't do the job, and he got really mad at Martin. So now we're using a guy named Joe. This may work, as Joe shaves him the old-fashioned way—taking him all the way down to the barber chair and laying him back. He hasn't argued with Joe yet, and Joe has been effective with him so far. Bill's face breaks out so badly if he is not shaved.

I told him his childhood friend Jim Sharp had died. He said, "Oh, poor Martha and Leonard." Those were Jim's parents who have been dead for 45 years. But for Bill to remember them amazed me. He must have loved Jim's parents. Then he said, "This will just kill Martha." I let it pass. A little later he said, "I can't believe Fuqua died." I said, "No, it was Jim Sharp." He looked at me and said, "Oh no! Not Sharpo." That is what Bill had called him as a teenager. Then he said, "Let's call Jim tomorrow."

DECEMBER 11, 2010

It seems like I've been with doctors all week. I'll go in Monday to get a complete knee replacement on the left knee. I went to see Bill. He's lost a lot more weight. I stocked him up on Dr. Peppers and peanut-butter crackers. I even put extra in the closet. He'll never look in the closet, but the aides or Suzanne will have them to restock with. I told him, "Look! There's lots more in the closet." I showed him right where I put them—right where anyone can see them. I closed the door and said, "Now, what's in that closet?" He said, "I don't know." I said, "Well, open the door and see." Bill said, "No, I can't go there." He will not open the closet door or the bathroom door. For some reason he thinks he is not supposed to do that. He has no idea what is behind the doors. Imagine being in a room for over three years and not opening the only two doors in the room except for the outside door.

Bill didn't look good today. He was listening to the loud music in the dining room—same old stuff. I said, "Oh, you are really liking this Christmas music." He said, "Okay." He was shaved and looked okay. I won't be back for at least two weeks, so I am worried about him. Suzanne and Tye will look after him. He is well taken care of, but I worry. Suzanne is sick. We're a pretty sorry bunch around here now. One is not a lot better off than the other.

End of the year. Have to go get the knee replacement.

This ends 2010 for Bill and Bebe.

Maybe a better 2011.

Happy New Year. It really is tough to be in the golden years.

2011

THE SLOW GOODBYE

Mind and Matter

I am so happy to be getting out of the therapy home. I'm still on a walker, but feeling much better. I'll have to continue therapy for two more weeks at least. When Suzanne picked me up, I insisted, against her advice, on going to see Bill before she took me home. I can barely get around, but I've been so worried about him. He knew Suzanne right off, but he didn't know me at all. When I said my name, he still didn't know. I thought I was going to cry. Of course I should have been more prepared. I was sentimental. He was just standing in his room doing nothing, but he was happy to see us and especially little Ben. My leg is in a huge black brace from hip to ankle, but Bill didn't seem to even notice. I said, "I have had surgery." He said, "Oh."

We didn't stay long, as I could tell it didn't matter to him, and I really didn't feel good. It is very tiring for me to even move around. I haven't seen him in 22 days, and he hadn't even missed me, or known that I hadn't been there all that time. It is so sad to think about. I just keep thinking, Does he ever have a thought? At least he is kind and loving, and Betty, the head nurse, said they had celebrated a 105-year-old woman's birthday last week. Bill sang and danced so long

that they had to put him in a wheelchair to take him to bed.
I think he's having more fun than he ever had before (joke),
but I sure wish things were like they used to be.

JANUARY 6, 2011

I drove over to see Bill, and he was just sitting in the dining room with a black man and an old woman. All of them
were just staring. I hobbled over, and when he saw me he
looked really hard and then asked, "Is it you?" I said, "Yes!"
He got up and hugged and hugged me. I thought he would
never turn me loose. Then he kissed my forehead and said,
"I thought you were gone forever." I really don't think he was
ever sure the other day who I was, but he just didn't think it
was me. He was certain today, and I looked right at him and
said, "Listen, let me tell you what has happened to me. I have
been very, very sick and had knee surgery." I showed him the
brace and all, and he said, "Oh, Bebe. Don't. You don't worry
any more. I will take care of you. You just rest and get well,
Bebe. I have to have you and you know that and I can take
good care of you."

I will tell you right now, he has always been the best
caregiver of me and the children when we were sick. He was
always so attentive and just took care of everything. When I
was bedridden with pregnancies, he would bring my meals
to the bed and brush my hair. Not too well, mind you, but
. . . . He was almost a too-attentive caregiver. The children
remember him always being the one who rocked and held
them when they were sick. He'd bring stuff to their bed for

them. He'd check on anyone who was sick. He didn't want me to leave today, but I knew I had to because I wasn't supposed to be out or driving. I wanted to get home before the kids found out that I was out driving. No one knew where I was, so I knew I'd better hit the road.

JANUARY 9, 2011

I spent the afternoon with Bill. I felt so bad I didn't think I could drive over, but it was worth it to see him so happy to see me. He was lying in bed, and I asked how he felt. He said he didn't know. Later we watched a movie, and I asked what he was thinking. He said, "I'm thinking what that man is thinking." That was funny. He looked down at my leg today and said, "What happened?" Of course, I told him the same story again. Again, he was so sorry for me and told me not to worry. He was quiet today. I have two more weeks of hard therapy, so I may not get to go as often. I just wear down completely.

JANUARY 22, 2011

I felt bad today, and my knee hurt a lot. I have a bad cold. Bill is not feeling well, either. He has a terrible chest cold and cough. We sat together and just watched TV. He snuggled under his comforter. Bad cough. I stayed until it was late and told them to give him something more for that cough. I was tired and went home. I took a pain pill and went to bed.

JANUARY 23, 2011

They had to take Bill to Corpus Christi to the hospital to catheterize him and clean out his throat. It was full of phlegm. They brought him back this evening and told me not to come. His stomach was hurting him badly.

JANUARY 24, 2011

Bill doesn't remember going to the hospital. He has diarrhea and feels really bad. He has that terrible cold. Just wants to be quiet, stay curled up in his comforter and lie still. He is all raw on his private parts and real sore there too, so he doesn't like for them to change his diapers.

JANUARY 26, 2011

My birthday: 78 (ugh). I saw a lot more wrinkles. Went over, but Bill and I were both *sick* sick. I didn't stay long. He is on a lot of medication.

FEBRUARY 2, 2011

It's so cold it's unbelievable. I went to therapy and then on to see Bill. Of course, he doesn't know the weather is terrible or anything. We drank coffee, and I told him Dorset and his girlfriend had been there. He didn't seem interested. He actually looked pretty good today. He'd had a nice shave and haircut, and he was wearing clean clothes, one of his good warm-up sweatshirts I had bought him earlier. He told me he had been working all morning long and was really worn out.

FEBRUARY 5, 2011

It's still bitter cold, and Bill was not feeling good today. His lower stomach hurt really bad. I asked the nurse for something to ease his pain. I just don't want him to have to be catheterized again. He just lay in bed. The Wisconsin people came to see him. Bill was nice, but he really did not feel like visiting anyone. I could tell he just wanted to be left alone. They stayed a long time even though I told them he really didn't feel good today. When they finally left, Bill looked at me and said, "Who the hell was that?" They really think he knows them all the time.

FEBRUARY 6, 2011

Finally, a nice day. Still cold, but not freezing. Bill was feeling good and didn't remember his stomach hurting yesterday. I said, "How's your tummy today?" He said, "Oh, fine. How's yours?" He was very anxious this afternoon and couldn't quite settle down in one spot. He kept thinking we were supposed to be going somewhere and asking when were we going to leave. He would say, "Is the car ready? Is everything ready? Have you got us packed?" It is always this time of day when his anxiety starts, but today it was a little more intense than usual.

I stayed a long time. They were getting the lounge ready for the Super Bowl. I asked whether he remembered the Green Bay Packers. He had loved them. He said yes, but I could tell he didn't. Fae was trying to get a bunch of us to go down and watch. She said they'd have popcorn, and she just happened to have a little flask of Scotch. But Bill wasn't interested, and really I wasn't either. My knee is still in the brace, and I have trouble getting around.

FEBRUARY 12, 2011

I felt bad all week. The weather was rainy and cold, down to zero at night. I didn't even get out this week. Suzanne took care of me and Bill both. I went over today, though, and Bill was at the nurses' station. Nurse Darcy, who I just love, was leading him to do a change. She saw me and said, "We gotta go change—we have a real mess." She had to get a male aide to help, and they had to take him and shower him completely, then I went in while they were dressing him. He's chapped, just like a baby with diaper rash. She said, "Bebe, we are trying. His skin is so sensitive, but we're doctoring him."

When Bill finally saw me, he said, "That's my wife." I got a John Wayne movie on, and he lay down just totally exhausted. Again he started getting anxious around 4 or 4:30. I am going to have to go directly to the doctor and talk to him. Bill can't remember a thing—not even the shower they just gave him. People tell me that most Alzheimer's patients remember lots of details from early years, but he doesn't. He just doesn't remember a thing. He cannot remember any year—early or not.

FEBRUARY 13, 2011

Bill feels awful today. He didn't even get out of bed. He looks so pale.

FEBRUARY 15, 2011

Bill has bad diarrhea again, and I don't think he ever really got over the last time. He is losing so much weight. He didn't want to eat or drink anything. I kept bringing crushed ice so I could get some liquid in him.

FEBRUARY 17, 2011

Bill slept nearly the whole time. He is just miserable today. He's sore in his private parts, and he had on wet pants. I had a fit, and they swore they had just changed him. He wouldn't let them shave him, and he's trying to fight them when they doctor him. He is just so raw. He doesn't want to be touched. The female aide said, "I'm afraid to try—he said he would hit me if I touched him." I said, "Well, let me." Bill threw her a kiss when she left. Then I said, "Let me put some good cream on you, and I promise it will help." He let me doctor him, and I was very careful to be gentle. I stayed a long time. It seems like he is feeling worse all the time.

FEBRUARY 27, 2011

Bill was feeling really bad and was so raw it was awful. I had brought over some good baby medicine (for diaper rash), but he didn't want me to touch him. Finally, I talked him into it. I got him doctored pretty well, but I had to quit because he was just so sore. Bill looks weaker and will eat nothing but the peanut-butter cookies. I know if we can get that skin better, he will feel better all over.

MARCH 1, 2011

I got a call at 8:30 that they're taking Bill to the hospital at Aransas Pass. They said he has had a really bad night, and they've given him everything they're allowed to give him. When I got to the hospital, the doctor there was calling in another doctor. They're doing all kinds of tests on him. We were in the ER all day long, and he was so restless. I kept asking the new doctor for his meds and told the nurse that there would be a problem if they didn't get his medicine. Finally, they gave him some, but he was so agitated by then that he was ready to try to take them out.

Finally, we got a room at 6:30—I had to go home. I told the nurses that he is a sundowner and to be sure to give those meds every four hours or else he will give them problems that they don't want. They all just smiled and said, "Don't worry, we have all kinds of patients here and know how to take care of them." This is one time I thought, Well, I warned you, so just get ready.

MARCH 2, 2011

The first thing when I walked in early this morning, the head nurse came running and told me that he really gave them hell last night around midnight. They had tried to catheterize him and he wouldn't let them. He told them he was getting up. He had all those IVs going in him and all hooked up, and the two nurses couldn't hold him down. He knocked one nurse against the wall, got out of bed pulling out IVs, and it took four people to get him back in bed. They had to give him one of those "quickie shots" that is like an instant tranquilizer. The nurse said, "Well, you know he looks so frail, but he is really strong." I loved it. I said, "Yes, I know. That is what I told you all last night." I was not sorry for them at all, but poor Bill had to go through getting all the IVs in again and still getting the catheter. When the evening crew came in, I started telling them he was a sundowner and to watch out. They just laughed and said, "Oh, we have already heard."

There's a Mexican-American man across the room from him and he must have 15 people visiting him at all times— crying babies and all. But they're nice people. Anyway, one of the young members of that family told me this morning that Bill had told him last night that he wanted to leave. Bill told him he was busted. The young guy said, "Well, I was just busted too, but they should go pretty easy on you." The old Mexican-American man started laughing and told his grandson that Bill means he is busted—out of money—not busted for drugs. Different kind of bust. He is calmer now—I'm sure they have him on enough medication to keep him calm. He won't let anyone feed him but me, and I mean he won't eat a bite. Then he will look at me and say, "Is this good, or crap?"

He is much calmer when I'm there, so I'm staying all day and just propping my leg up. He keeps asking if the car is ready "to roll" and then he says, "Well, let's hit the road." He still uses his old sayings. He is very polite to the nurses and still flirts with them, and says thank you and stuff like that. I just hate to see him in so much pain. Every time he pees, it burns and he yells. I know they are doing everything they can. Bill asked me, "How long have I lived?" Not how old he is. I said 81 years. He said, "Oh, no. You're crazy. I may have lived for 50 years, or 40."

Yesterday he wanted me to call his mom and dad and then to ask if Beth and Eula (my parents) were coming. He suddenly said things that he hasn't ever said, and he brought up things that haven't been said before, or in a long time. I just said that everything was fine, but kind of enjoyed the talk. I did ask him if he remembered the ranch, and after a while he said, "I think so." Then I said, "Where is it?" He looked right at me and said, "Well, Bebe, don't you know?" I asked him again and he said, "You know I'm gonna croak." I said, "No, you aren't. You've been telling me that for over 50 years to just try to make me sad and cry. And you're not dead yet, so just shut up with that story." Then he said, "Well, will I die before you?" I said, "Yes." He said, "I hope so, 'cause you have to take care of me."

MARCH 3, 2011

I got over to the hospital early and he was *ready to go* (somewhere). Finally, at 4:00 this afternoon he was released and they let me take him back to the home. I told the doctor he would do better if I could take him, but to be sure and give him a good strong pill before I pulled out. When I got him in the car, he looked at all the cars in the parking lot and just nearly had a fit. He said, "Where did all those cars come from? They are going to hit us." I explained that they were just parked there, so when we got on the highway, all he did was holler at me. He just knew we were going to have a wreck or someone was going to run into us. Then when I would go around a car, he would say, "Are you trying to kill us?"

It was a big relief to get him back to the home. They were waiting with his wheelchair and loaded him in. He recognized the place as a motel we have stayed in before, and he was immediately comfortable with the regular surroundings. The nurse turned to me and said, "Leave now. We'll take over. Please don't come back for a day or two as we have to get him back into routine." They do know how to handle Bill and do a perfect job. He loves them all. I do realize he is exactly where he needs to be. Tired, I headed back home.

What's in His Mind?

I lost some notes, but nothing important. He was waking up today when I got there, and he said he felt good. His hair looked terrible, so I laughed and showed it to him in the mirror. He said, "Oh that's terrible. What can we do?" I said, "Well, I will wet it and brush it, so put your hands under the faucet and wet your hair." It got so funny. He would put his hands in the water, but not catch any—and he'd never put his hands on his hair. He couldn't understand what I meant—getting water from faucet to hands to hair. We both got to laughing. Finally, I got it wet and brushed and we watched a movie. When I said I had to go he said, "Okay. I'll stay right here."

Bill was standing in the hall when he saw me. He started waving at me. He looked good and seemed happy today. We got some coffee and ice for him to chew on. We were watching a show, and when the actors ordered some ice cream, he said, "Oh, I want some ice cream right now." I said, "Okay, in a little while." He loves ice cream and used to eat it every night before bedtime at home. He's like our son Mitch, who loves vanilla best. I will pick some up next time.

MARCH 19–20, 2011

Bill was not feeling good today and just wanted to lie around. He was actually more alert yesterday than today. He seems tired, and when I tried to get him up to change his clothes, which were pretty bad, he couldn't get off the bed. So I had to get help. When I tried pulling him up, he just pulled me down—it was funny. I got him changed, and he wanted to lie right back down. He didn't say anything when I left.

MARCH 22–24, 2011

Bill was shaved and looked really good today. It was bingo day, and oh, he hates it more than ever. The Wisconsin man had come and gotten him, telling him he would enjoy it. Bill will go anywhere someone tells him to. Then the Wisconsin couple came back to the room and started talking to me about what a terrible thing it is for someone to lose their mind—*right in front of Bill.* I got the subject changed, and Bill never caught on to a bit of it. But I didn't like it. These Wisconsinites are just a little too much for me.

Bill had wanted to lie down and wrap up. He didn't want me to leave today, and he followed me to the main station. Betty came out and started talking. He was holding onto me for dear life, and then an aide came and she just started walking him toward the dining room. I slipped out. He has gotten pretty good about my going, but there are still some bad days. Today he just grabbed me and kept saying, "I don't want you to go. Let's just stay here." I can't leave when he does that, so I wait until it works out.

He was feeling insecure and said he had the "jingle jangles" today. I have a meeting on his evaluation next week, where I'll suggest that they start giving him something earlier than 4:00. This has always been a bad time for him.

MARCH 26, 2011

Bill refused to let them shave him today and felt really bad. He just wanted to lie around. He stared at the air vent. He didn't talk at all.

MARCH 27, 2011

Bill still wasn't shaved and felt quite bad. He said his good eye hurt. It was extremely red, and he kept his blind eye closed (he usually does now). I told the nurse, who got a warm cloth. I kept it on his eye for a while. He said that helped. I called the doctor, who will prescribe some eye medicine. I can't let anything happen to that one good eye.

MARCH 29, 2011

I met with four people for the evaluation and listened to them. Then when it came my time, I told them that I did not intend to put up with him not being shaved. He has rosacea and always has, and he needs to be shaved and treated every day. They all wrote in their little books and swore he'd be shaved every day except Sunday, when the men aren't there to shave, and Bill won't let the women. I agreed to that. Then I went on down to see Bill. His eye was much better. He didn't even know it had been hurting, so I guess the medicine worked. He sat in his chair a little while today.

He had had another run-in with one of the part-time nurses. He was up at the nurses' station, just standing and walking around as he does all the time. She said, "Bill, what are you doing?" He just looked at her. She walked around and took his arm and said, "You get back to your room." He looked at her and shook her arm off and said, "You go to hell and don't touch me." He shook her arm off him and didn't move an inch. The Wisconsin man was walking by and walked over and said, "Hey Bill, how's it goin'? How about some coffee?" Then he turned to the aide and said, "I got that on my phone and will turn you in." Bill went right with his Wisconsin friend for a coffee. I guess I have to hand it to the Wisconsin people. They do watch out for Bill. Thank God. I have told them, and the main nurses have told all of the workers, "Don't tell Bill directly what to do." All the regulars know it. Well, this is the first third of the year. Wonder what the rest of it will hold for the Bralleys.

APRIL 1–2, 2011

Bill was very restless. We walked as long as he could shuffle. He lost his balance and nearly fell. Finally, I gave up and went back to the room. He was fidgety and said he had the "jingle jangles" again. He was shaking badly, and when I took his hand it was shaking more than I have ever seen it shake. It seems Bill is deteriorating more all the time in his movements, and his shaking is worse—much worse. He tries so hard to make conversation, and he'll start off and then just say, "Oh, you know." Then he'll point at the clock or the A/C vent.

He doesn't know anything—even what happened five minutes ago. He is always wondering where he is and doesn't know his room, so he still thinks he is in the wrong place. He still speaks to everyone and even though I have told him Skip's name over and over, he will still call him "the no-leg man."

The ladies all love him, and it is almost a chorus when he goes in the dining room. They all sing out, "Hi, Bill—I'm missing you." He goes into his show-biz act and waves and throws them kisses. Then he will stop and look around to see if he has spoken to all the ladies, and they just love it. I hear them saying, "Isn't he adorable? Isn't he sweet?" They pay no attention at all to me, as if I were just an aide or something.

APRIL 5, 2011

Bill was in the hall again and wouldn't let them shave him. He looked bad, and of course the Wisconsin people came by. I already knew it; sometimes he gets so stubborn. So I said, "Let's get some ice." When we got to his room, he said, "Can we go in here?" I said yes, and he said, "Where is this?" As he sat staring off in space, I asked, "Bill, what are you thinking?" And he said, "Oh, I was just thinking about Henry Blackburn." That is a friend he had in about the 5th grade and probably hasn't seen in 40 years. I asked, "Well, what about Henry?" He said, "Well, I don't know. Just thought about Henry." Why would he remember Henry Blackburn and not know his own room? His arm was still bloody—all blue and so tender. He falls a lot, so I keep putting good cream on it—gently.

APRIL 7, 2011

Bill was very restless. He has been on edge all week. I don't know what it is, but he is very anxious. He won't watch any TV. He shuffles slowly but wants to keep moving. He tried to start sentences about three times and would get really frustrated and just say, "Hell, I don't know. You know." I just say yes. I know he wants to tell me something.

APRIL 8, 2011

I got a call from the home. Bill came to blows with a man in a wheelchair. They said that Bill didn't start it but that he sure finished it. They wouldn't tell me who the other person was, but I will bet it was Earl. They said the other person was mad and ran into Bill with his wheelchair. Bill didn't fall but turned around madder than hell and started swinging. They rushed to get to them when the man hit Bill a good one and rammed him against the wall with his chair. Neither one was hurt, but of course Bill was bleeding all over. It's that thin skin where he was burned with anhydrous ammonia when he was farming at the irrigation farm in Groom. They bandaged him up and took him right in to supper, and he didn't even know what had happened. Hope the other guy is over his mad spell.

APRIL 9, 2011

Bill was just lying in bed when I got there and had awakened from his nap. Of course he was wet all over. I got his wet pants off and some dry ones on. As I was putting his shirt on, he said, "Oh, you are hurting me." I said, "I'm sorry, just trying to get your shirt on." And he said, "If you hurt me again, I'm going to leave you and never come back." I said, "Oh, I won't hurt you again. I don't want you to leave me." Then he said, "Well, you had better be good to me." He can talk in a sentence sometimes—when he wants to and when he knows exactly what he wants to say. Of course, he will forget it just as quickly. His arms are black and blue and swollen—they just look terrible.

Tye had been to see him at lunch, so I said, "Well, have any of the kids been here today?" He said, "No, I was busy all day long and saw no one." Tye was there at noon, and now it is 3. No memory at all. He is so thin, his clothes are hanging off him. Tomorrow night I am having the Winter Texans (the Wisconsinites) for dinner, and they are really excited. The man told me that he told Bill about it and said, "Man, I sure wish you were going to be there with us." I'm sure that meant a lot to Bill. They are going to get to taste some good Texas dove.

APRIL 13, 2011

They were bathing and shaving Bill when I got there, and the doctor was there. So it gave me a good chance to visit with him. He said, "Bebe, you know Bill is in the very last stages of Alzheimer's. In my opinion, you will see him deteriorating more all the time. You may have some hard decisions to make—sooner than we thought. But I know your feelings. I feel that you are prepared, and we can work together." He also said he was ordering a new cream for Bill's face.

Bill was so tired after all the bathing, so I got him back to his room and yet—you guessed it—he pottied in his pants. So we had to do it all over again. *Just after the bath!* He is bandaged all over his arms, so we must be careful changing him. He was able to eat peanut-butter crackers and drink his Dr. Peppers. When we were walking in the hall, he heard someone and said, "Was that Bebe?" I said, "No, I am right here." He just said, "Oh, yeah." When I asked him what he had been doing, he looked at the big clock on the wall and said, "Well, I was busy on that." The clock doesn't run. It always says 5 o'clock. He pointed at it and said they came through there and now they are gone. Later he had a big yellow cat on his bed, and he just loved that.

Easter party. I absolutely hate these things. Seems they are always at the wrong time. The party was from 1:30 until 4:00. That's Bill's nap time, but I got there and got him all dressed up. Then he said, "I'm not going to any party." It seems I've heard this story before. Anyway, I got him looking good and then he just lay down on the bed and said, "You can't get me up." He covered up with the comforter and I could tell he was going to stay right there. So I told the girl to bring him some strawberry shortcake, and he would not even eat it. He picked at the big strawberries on the top, so I just dumped everything in the trash. He wouldn't look at the Easter Bunny when he came to his room. He turned his face to the wall.

Of course the Wisconsin people came joyfully and helped spread the cheer. They wanted to say goodbye, as they were heading back to Wisconsin until next winter. They told Bill how they'd miss him, and they'd be back and all kinds of sappy stuff. When they left, he asked, "Who the hell was that?" They are really nice people. She made me a pretty afghan as a going-away gift. Which really surprised me, but it was so kind of her. They just love donating their time and work to the home. I could never do that. But it is nice to have people who do. I'd rather take a dull butcher knife to my own throat.

APRIL 17, 2011

I went to see Bill, and he was asleep so I just watched TV until he woke up. He's always happy to wake up and find me there. We were both rather tired today, and when I got home and fed my livestock (the cat and the dog), I went to bed—with them.

APRIL 19, 2011

Bill had wandered off, and when he saw me he threw out his hands toward me, just holding out his hands until we reached each other. He was just glad to be "found." Very quiet today.

MAY 13, 2011

It's Friday the 13th. Bill was listening to music—a pretty good guitar player who sang all the old songs, but Bill was just staring with that completely blank look. I went in and hugged him, and he looked up at me like he had never seen me before in his life. But he smiled and said, "Hello" politely. I sat down beside him and said, "Do you know who I am?" He said, "Yes." I said, "Well, what's my name?" He looked at me (politely) and said, "I can't think right now." I kept at him and said, "Well, how do you know me?" He looked at me again like I was bothering him and said, "I can't remember right now." So I told the nurse that he didn't even know me today, and she came over and said, "Bill, this is your pretty wife." He said, "Well . . . ." Finally she said, "Who is your wife?" And he said, "Bebe." And she said, "Is this Bebe?" He just smiled and she finally said, "Bill, this is Bebe." He looked at me strangely, and I held out my hand.

He seemed to feel better but he had stomach pains. I said, "Do you want to walk a little?" And he said, "Yes." We went to the room and when we got there, he said we couldn't go in there. Then he looked at me and said, "I have to get the oil changed and we will leave then." He may have begun to think I was Bebe, but I'm still not sure. I know for sure he didn't know me a while ago, and I'm not sure about now. He can hardly shuffle. Only very slowly. And he doesn't know where he's going. He stays cold all the time. It is just so pitiful. I don't know how long he can go on this way. It is certainly no life at all. He doesn't know his room, doesn't know where to eat, can't use a fork and knife. When they take him to eat they have to push gently on his shoulder and tell him to sit down.

MAY 14, 2011

Today was a little different. Bill cannot remember my name, but he knows me. When I came in, he was all huddled in the comforter, and he opened his eye and said, "Oh, you are here! I'm glad." I went and hugged him and said, "Well, what's my name?" He laughed and said, "I can't think of that. But I know you. Oh yeah. Nellie Bebe." We laughed again.

He tried to tell me something but couldn't make it come out. Finally he looked at me straight in the eyes and said, "I wish I had my mind back." So he knows there is something wrong—very badly wrong. No one has ever told me that Alzheimer's patients knew things like that. I said, "Yes, Bill there is something wrong." He said, "I think I died and I am just here in between." I said, "Well, I don't know." Then he said, "I nearly think and then everything just floats away—I don't like this."

I got a good Western movie on, although he doesn't understand them anymore. The words the actors say come into his ears wrong, and he will say "Did they say?" I'll say no and tell him what they said, which will be something totally different. At one point he laughed and said, "I'm not crazy—I have just lost my mind." My God, that is so true.

I want to talk to the psychiatrist about this—and several other things Bill has said. Has anyone else ever said things like this? He felt good today, and when I said I had to go, he said I'd never make it back for the show. I said to remember what happens and tell me later. He laughed again and said, "Don't count on that." A girl came on the commercial that had a big nose and wild hair, and he started laughing and said, "God, she's ugly." He was really cute and funny today, so when I started to leave I said, "Now say my name before I leave." He said again, "You'd better just go."

MAY 15, 2011

Bill never ceases to amaze me. Today he was standing at the nurses' station with the nurses—right in the middle of them as they were working and giving medicine to people. He was just *standing with them*. He never turns around and looks behind him, so the nurses started laughing and he laughed with them. They said, "Bill, look behind you." Finally, one of the girls walked over and turned him around. He *grabbed* me and said, "I've been looking for you! Is the car ready? Is the car here?" I said, "Yeah, but let's get some coffee first." And of course he said okay.

We went to get coffee and Bill patted every lady in there on the arm or shoulder. Once I got the coffee he said, "Well, are we ready?" I said, "Well, we need to go down to get a few things out of the room." When we got to the room I had to assure him that it was all right to go in. I quickly got a movie on, and Bill lay down and pulled up the comforter and just stared off into space. Seems like he was better today than he has been in a very long time. Perhaps I'm no judge at all. He tried to tell me something several times today but couldn't get it out. He would just laugh and say, "Well, you know." I always say, "Yeah, of course."

MAY 19, 2011

Bill was all the way down the east hall just looking out the window—he looked so frail and helpless standing there. I walked down, and when I was nearly to him I said, "Bill! Bill!" Finally, he turned sideways and kind of looked at me but didn't move. He seemed not to know me at all. Then, as I got very close, within a foot of him, he burst into a big smile and held out his arms and said (for the first time in a long time), "Bebe! Bebe! *I have been looking for you!*" We slowly walked back up the hall and barely made it to his room. He was totally exhausted, and I was afraid he would fall. He lay down and reached out for my hand. He covered up and just lay there. He doesn't watch TV anymore. I stayed until he dozed off, slipped my hand out, and left.

MAY 21, 2011

Bill was sound asleep when I got there. I turned on the TV and made some noise, finally waking him briefly. He just smiled a little and closed his eyes again. He never did get up or fully wake up, so I left right before 5 because I didn't want to be there when they woke him to eat and then have to leave him.

MAY 22, 2011

Tye had been there to spend lunch with him and called to tell me he thought Bill was doing well today and ate a good lunch. Tye laughed and said, "I think Daddy thought I was going to pick the plate up, so he ate really fast." I went over a little earlier than usual, and when I got there Bill was right in the middle of the nurses' station. I laughed and said, "Well, do you all have a new nurse?" They laughed and said, "Yeah, he comes right in the station sometimes and likes to stand here." He was all smiles. I said, "Well, do you want to go get some coffee?" And then we walked a little bit. Pretty soon he was all worn out and shaking so much he could hardly stand anymore.

MAY 26, 2011

It is family night again, and both Bill and I detest it. I know they have to do it. They go to a whole lot of work for this. The first thing Amy told me when I got there was, "Bill isn't shaved. He threw a big fit and he said he isn't going to let anyone shave him. We had to tell him that you would be mad at him if he didn't let us shave him, so he let us shave him a little." Then I saw Bill wandering around looking completely frustrated, with all the people gathering. As I went up to him, he looked lost and said, "What are they pulling?" Then he started whispering, and I couldn't hear a thing. Anyway, I saw a table out in the hall and said, "Let's go out there." He threw his hands in the air and said, "Okay."

We went to the farthest table and he asked if the car was ready to go. I said yes but that I thought we should eat first. He whispered something about the food, which was chicken-fried chicken, corn, mashed potatoes, and gravy. He looked at it. I cut the meat up, and then he took his bread and tried to dip it in the corn. I said, "Why don't you just eat the bread with your hand?" He looked at me and just laid it down. He doesn't know the foods anymore—can't tell one from the other. I fed him a little with a spoon, and he ate a little bit. Then he would try to eat one tiny piece of corn at a time.

Finally, they brought the dessert around and I asked, "Do you want cake or pie?" He just stared, so I took some chocolate cake for him. I would put a piece on the fork and hold it to his mouth, and he would eat it.

He was cold all evening and wanted to "go home," so we went to the room and he lay down. I told Margaret (a favorite nurse) as we walked by that he was sleepy, and she said just to run on. She took Bill on down to the room. He could barely move. He can still walk, but it's a shuffle and very, very slow. He cannot do things he did only a few weeks ago.

A Kind of Renewed Vow

Bill never got out of bed today. He was wrapped up in the comforter, and his pants were on the floor. He was cold and wet. I washed, dried, and cleaned him. It's a good thing Toni bought two comforters because we need them both. After I got him all re-dressed, he just cuddled up in the fresh, clean comforter and bed and never talked until he looked at me and said, "I don't want a divorce." Plain as day, not whispering as he usually does. I said, "Oh, I don't either—so we won't get a divorce." He smiled and said, "Good." That is the only clear sentence he has said in a long time.

He doesn't understand instructions like "stand up." He'll scoot back when I tell him to get up off the bed. When I take both hands and say to pull, to get him up, he pulls me down on top of him. I get tickled and he looks at me as if it say, "What's wrong?" We keep doing it and I laugh. When I laugh, he always laughs. Just because I laugh. He always has his shoes on the wrong foot. He simply cannot respond to any instruction anymore.

Here is where we are now:

He can't tell when he needs to go to the bathroom at all. He has to be cared for and changed like a baby.

He's had a complete loss of coordination. He can still shuffle a little, but with very poor balance. He wanders as much as he can down the halls or into rooms, and of course he never knows where he is. He falls a lot.

He can't speak a sentence anymore, although he will still try to tell me something. Now he just makes circles with his hands instead of talking—I don't know what he means. The nurses say he communicates with them that way too, but they don't know what he wants either.

When other people talk to him, he mostly smiles and just looks at them or just stares. He can't answer anything except with *yes* or *no*, and then it may be inappropriate. He mostly whispers now. Very seldom does he speak out loud. I can't understand a thing when he does that, and I thought maybe my hearing was going. Suzanne says she can't understand him either.

He is very shaky all over, especially in his hands and particularly in individual fingers. He stays cold all the time, no matter how hot the room is.

He doesn't know whether he is hungry or full. He'll reach and eat more cookies and will try to drink the Dr. Pepper out of the wrong side of the can (it runs down his face).

He still doesn't know where his room is, or the bathroom.

He can't tell time—he will look at the big clock on the wall and point to it and whisper slowly. He doesn't know directions—like north, south, west, or east.

None of his pictures of family and friends mean a thing to him anymore.

He doesn't even attempt to watch TV. I have been taking a little tape recorder and playing old favorite songs. It seems to relax him, but he doesn't know the tunes.

He recognizes me most of the time, but not all the time. And very seldom does he know my name.

MAY 31, 2011

Bill was sitting in the dining room, and they were playing bingo—which he still hates, but now they don't even try to make him play. They just let him shuffle around and do as he pleases. I brought him a chocolate sundae from Dairy Queen. He loves these. When he saw me and the sundae he tried to get to me through the bingo people in wheelchairs and became very frustrated when he couldn't get around them. Another man visiting his mother caught on and jumped up and helped get Bill through to me. We smiled—both of us know the situation—Bill hugged the man for helping him, and the man was so nice.

Anyway, he was so happy to see me. We went down to his room for him to eat his sundae. When I handed it to him, he just sat there and opened his mouth, so I fed him until he said no. He lay down and tried to tell me something. As always, he couldn't get it out but kept trying. Finally he started making circles. He smiled and said, "I want to tell you." Then nothing made sense, and he knew it. He just looked so sad and lay down. He knows everything is wrong, but he doesn't understand and of course doesn't know what to do about it.

He kept looking at me, pointed to the clock, and said, "You know." He did the circles, and I said, "Yes, I know."

When he looks at me as he did today, I can tell he knows things are not right and he will almost look through me with that one good eye. I think he is hoping I can read his thoughts and will know what he wants to say, or else that I can do something to make things all better. He dozed off, and I slipped out. It's just so sad. No one should have to live like this.

JUNE 2, 2011

I got there early, as I was taking all new clothes. I showed them all to him, and he smiled but never got out of bed. I took the old clothes and told Amy to give them to some others who needed things. There are men there with hardly any clothes, and they are just worn-out looking. I said, "Just cover the Bralley name and pass them on." This was the second time this week I have seen a wheelchair in his room, but I have been getting him up and he can shuffle a little. I went and asked Margaret, "Why is there a wheelchair in Bill's room?" She said, "Bebe, Bill is not walking as well as he was last week and is falling a lot. He's so feeble that it is safer for us to take him to the dining room in his chair." We did have him in therapy for walking but I can tell he is simply getting weaker all the time. Now his body is going as well as his mind. His balance is terrible.

Today I looked at him and said, "Bill, what are you thinking?" He laughed and hit his head with his fist and very plainly said, "I'm *trying* to think." He will look at me so sad and just shake his head and do the circles and point in the air. I tried to get him to remember a few little things today. He reached over and took both my hands and shook his head and said, "No. No." I just don't know what to expect next.

JUNE 4, 2011

Bill definitely is not improving. He mostly just lies around. I got him up a little today, and he just took a few steps and stopped and stared at the A/C vent. Then he went back to the bed.

JUNE 9, 2011

Bill was sitting in a chair next to the nurses' desk, just staring straight ahead. I tapped on the glass as I walked in. He was looking that way. When he saw me, he opened his arms and reached out for me and started smiling. He seemed so happy to see me. He looked good and was more alert than he has been for a while. I took some pictures, and one of the aides took one of Bill and me. He really looked better than I have seen him in a long time. He was restless, though, and I got the TV on but something in the story made him really nervous. I switched and we just sat and had our drinks.

JUNE 12, 2011

My mother's birthday. Bill was in the wheelchair right next to the nurses and was happy to see me. I could tell right off something was wrong, and he was frustrated. I said, "Let me get you some ice and me some coffee and we will find a little table in the hall." He looked desperate. Finally, Martin came by and said, "Okay, Bill, I have to take you to your room and get you all cleaned up." He took him away. Poor Bill's hands were shaking so much he couldn't hold his ice cup. He started whispering, and I couldn't understand a thing. I said, "Let's go out and move around."

We went down the hall. He had a terrified look on his face and I asked, "Honey, what's the matter?" He said (loud enough for me to hear), "I am so scared." Then he would just look completely blank. He is shaking so much, and he hits his knees to try to make them stop. Then he looked at me and said, "We have to go." He was very nervous. Then he said, "I'm fainting." I helped him out of the chair and into bed. He was really cold, so I covered him up. He wanted to hold my hands. I tried to get him to relax, but he stayed tense for at least an hour.

It was dinner time. I said, "Bill, I'm going to check the nurse a minute." I told them how agitated he was; they said he had been that way all afternoon, starting about noontime. They were watching him. It sure worries me. I see changes that we haven't had before. He had such a distant look in his eye and simply knows nothing. *Blank*. I can tell that would be scary—not knowing. I am scared for him.

JUNE 14, 2011

I met with Amy and another nurse, and it was a good meeting. I believe we are all on the same page with Bill. I found out that Bill had hit one of the aides over the weekend. I felt bad about that—that's not the true Bill. He gets mad when they bathe, shave, and dress him like a kid. He tries to make them stop. I thought the button shirts would help, but he gets so mad at the other things, and he has to be shaved. They always test for urinary-tract infections. He has had several. But he didn't have one this time. He's just agitated, I guess.

He was sitting in the dining room all alone with his glass of lemonade. But he got that big smile when he saw me. We tried walking a little, but he tired out and went to the room. He is seeing things that aren't there and is scared of them. Today he spoke. He said, "I am scared for you." I told him I was okay and not to worry.

He is shaking worse—if that's possible. I told them, "No more speech therapy. Quit sticking him for blood sugar. If he has high sugar, so what." I told them today that I do not want anything to prolong his life. Just keep him comfortable and do what he needs and wants. He is not to be force-fed. I will allow him to eat with his fingers or they can feed him by spoon. They told me he's in the very last stages. My God, I knew that. That's when I said, "I know—that's why I want him comfortable but no extras to prolong life."

JUNE 17, 2011

Didn't go over today but got a call. Bill fell in the dining room. They said he isn't hurt. He tripped over someone else's wheelchair and fell on his butt. He's okay. I will go tomorrow.

JUNE 19, 2011

He slept most of the time. I tried talking to him, but he simply couldn't make sense or understand me. He seemed to be trying to tell me something several times, but just couldn't. The only thing I could understand that made any sense was when I said, "Did Tye come to see you today?" He said, "Yes. Came early." (He didn't.) I talked to Tye later, and he had gone by a couple of days ago—but not today. I tried to see if he could remember Amarillo today, as that is where he always wants to go. But he just looked at me blankly but as if he were trying. He looks at me intensely. It is hard to describe. *Very intensely* and directly in my eyes. The expression makes it seem as if he is wanting to tell me something so badly. Sometimes it looks like a help cry. I know very well that he knows this isn't right, but he doesn't know what to do. It's as if he is encased in a body and head that don't work no matter how hard he tries. Maybe that is what he keeps trying to tell me. I play more music—the oldies—and he will smile when one of our favorite songs plays. So I know he recognizes that music. He stays all covered like a baby.

JUNE 21, 2011

This is the day my Daddy died in 1984. Today little Ben started swimming lessons. Bill stayed curled up in bed the whole time I was there. He stared at me and then would try to tell me something, and then just quit. He seemed disgusted with himself. I took him ice cream sandwiches, but that was a mistake as it got all over him. I'm going to just stick to Dixie Cups. He loves his ice cream. Bill mostly stared at the wall and I talked like a machine trying to get his attention. I know he hears very little of what I say, and it means nothing. Sometimes he acts like he knows when I tell him something. I said, "Do you remember Sam Attebury?" (They went through grade school and high school together.) He looked and me and said, "Yeah." I said, "Well, Sam had a bad stroke." He said, "Oh." I could tell he just answered because he thought I wanted an answer.

JUNE 26, 2011

Bill has another urinary infection and will go to the doctor soon. I hate to put him through this again. But they are insisting. He just hates it. They called me this morning after breakfast to say that he had fallen from his wheelchair. When I got there, I held his hand. It shakes so badly you can hardly hold it. I have never seen anyone shake like this. I thought maybe trying to walk would help, but he shook his head no. He was very anxious and tried to get up out of his chair and nearly fell again. I took him to his room and helped him into bed. He was shaking so badly that the entire bed was shaking.

I started playing some music, and when I played "King of the Road" by Roger Miller, he opened his mouth and actually sang along with it and said some of the words quite plainly. But then he shut off. When I played Satchmo, he waved his hands and smiled. That proves to me he does remember something. But the tapes started bothering him, so I guess I will have to think up a new trick to try to bring out "Bill." He really is not responding to anything anymore. He just shakes and stays curled up all the time. I know he is going downhill fast.

JUNE 28, 2011

When I started into Bill's room, he was hanging onto the door as if he would fall if he turned loose. They had already called after he fell from his wheelchair this morning—right after breakfast. I took his hand, and he was shaking so much it was terrible. I said, "Hold on. Let's get back to your bed." I have never seen anyone shake like that; it is really unbelievable. He held on tightly, and when we got back to the bed, it was like he was caught and didn't know what to do. His entire body was very cold. I covered him well and held his hand, hoping that it would help the shaking. And I swear he turned a different color right before my eyes. The shaking stopped, his eyes closed. He was completely still, white and frozen-looking. I thought, oh my God, he's died. After about four seconds I felt him breathing again—finally. I don't know whether he stopped breathing or what. But it frightened me. He just relaxed after that, but the shaking had stopped and he kept his eyes closed. I stayed almost an hour longer, then slipped out. He never turned or moved the whole time. I know he is getting worse much faster than I thought would ever happen.

JULY 1, 2011

Bill was asleep when I got there, so I went to get coffee. Betty, the head RN, stopped me in the hall and said, "Bebe, I want to start Bill on a new extra-strength protein drink and also coconut pills. I have heard the coconut pills really help Alzheimer's patients." I said, "Well, okay. Let's do the drink, but I will have to read up on the coconut pills. I'll let you know tomorrow." I had to wake Bill up, but he wanted to go back to sleep. The aide told me that he had slept nearly all day and hadn't moved. I said, "Let's get him up." We finally got him up and in the chair. He got very irritated with us and got angry at the girl taking his blood pressure.

When she left, he looked at me and I could tell he was angry. I can always tell when he is angry—I can tell what he means by his eye expressions. I said, "Are you mad at me?" and as plain as day he said, "Yes." I asked why. He looked right at me so mad and said, "I'm gone." I asked again and he looked right at me and said, "I can't do." I leaned over and hugged him and said, "Bill, I'm sorry. I am doing everything I can to help you and it is all right to be mad at me. If there is anything I can do now, let me know. And I will do anything." He softened a little and took my hand and shook his head. Then he raised my hand and kissed it, and then three more little kisses. He just looked at me so pitiful as if he wanted out of this body and life. He said "hurt." I asked where and he circled his whole body and said "here."

He is barely eating, and only soft foods. They have to feed him with little spoons. They said they thought he could use a fork and that he could feed himself, but they can't depend on that! He simply won't eat. That irritated me. I said, "Well, *feed him by spoon*. He damn sure doesn't have to feed himself." He is requiring more water and ice all the time, as he dries out so readily. I think these are definitely Bill's last days. I don't see how he can hold on much longer. He is always in pain. I just hate seeing him this way, and I know Bill hates this life so much. He's lost all control of everything in his life and body, and I think he wants the end to come. It is just so sad and he is just a skeleton.

JULY 2, 2011

I read up on all of Betty's suggestions, and I do not agree with her. So I wrote a letter to Betty and told her I do not want Bill on the coconut pill or the protein drink—he hates that drink. She will not like this, but I don't want to try things to prolong Bill's life now, and the articles I read don't suggest these things would do any good anyway. I cannot even think of prolonging and putting Bill through more hell. Why would I want to force him to do things? If Bill could speak up, he would say, "Bebe, shoot me for God's sake. Don't let me live like this." I do know Bill's feelings.

I am tired of the idea of trying. We have tried many things, but nothing has worked a bit. We're just putting Bill through more pain and unhappiness. They keep saying, "Well, it might work—might prolong his life." I have read it all, and so far nothing has come along to provide a good healthy life that Bill could enjoy.

I am hoping to bring him home for his last few months of life. He looks at me so pitifully as if he is begging me to do something and I *can't*. I have a feeling that we are nearing the end, but I realize it could be two or three years, or more. How he can even hold out until the end of this year I don't know. I want him to pass normally and peacefully. Bill and I discussed this years ago, before he ever got sick. We both signed medical agreements: no life support or extraordinary means of support.

Bill slept nearly the whole time I was there today. He didn't have any pants on, just his diaper and shirt. Since this is a weekend, the staff is short of help. I am going back again today to clean him and dress him. Sometimes I feel so helpless. What to do? I am tired of having to fight with nurses and staff to keep him shaved and bathed, and to have clean clothes on. I have to take care of Bill; he would do the same for me.

My Good-Looking Husband

JULY 5, 2011

Today Bill is much better. I could hardly believe how good he looked. He spoke about four sentences and tried so hard to tell me something two or three times. He tried to watch a little TV and told me that "they got in a fight last night." I asked if he was in it, and said, "No—stayed out of it." Then he smiled and said, "We fight all the time." He was in a really good mood and talking a lot. Of course, he said, "Well, when are we going?" I answered, "Pretty soon." Then I asked him when he wanted to go, and where. He looked at me and said, "Not now." I said, "Oh, you want to wait a while?" He nodded. Soon he said, "Let's just stay right here." Of course I said okay. I pulled him up and said, "Let's walk a little." I got him to shuffle down the hall. We would sit down in the hall for a little while, then shuffle some more.

Finally, we made it all the way to the dining room, and three voices rang out as we walked in: "Bill's place is over here. Bring him here!" When we got there, the fat man said, "I've been saving it!" He seemed happy to see them all, and after I got him seated I said, "I will go back and get my coffee." I slipped out. He seemed better than he has in weeks, and I left feeling more up. Can't figure it out.

JULY 6, 2011

Bill is really sick again, with a fever. He's hurting all over. They have already put him on antibiotics for a urinary-tract infection. That really pulls him down.

JULY 7, 2011

Bill seemed better and was just waking up when I got there. They had a prison movie on. He would glance at it once in a while, but I could tell he couldn't follow the story. I said, "Let me pull you up and we'll walk a little." He held out his arms and I pulled him up. He put his arm around my waist, I was holding him, and we were heading toward the door when a prisoner shouted, *"Don't move, or I'll shoot you dead!"* Bill grabbed me to his chest and said "shush-h-h!" in my ear, holding me tightly. I said, "Oh, come on" and he put his other hand over my mouth and said "Sshhushhhh!" in my ear. I started edging us to the door and whispered, "We can get out here." We slowly scooted out the door and his heart was beating 100 miles an hour as he held onto me for dear life. He was an absolute nervous wreck. I knew he thought they were right behind us holding guns on us—ready to shoot. Finally, we got out the door, and a little aide came by and said, "Hey, Bill! You doing all right?" He waved at her and had instantly forgotten about the shooter.

Again we shuffled to the dining room. I got him seated next to Gilbert, the fat man, who immediately said, "This is Bill's place!" The two old women across from him were pointing to me, and I heard one say, "She belongs to Bill." He seemed happy now and ready for dinner—feeling so much better after the severe pain of yesterday.

JULY 14, 2011

Bill was all curled up, cold and wet. He didn't want to move, but I wanted to change him so I called for help. Darcy came and said he had fallen three times since I was last there. I had been to San Antonio on Monday, Tuesday, and Wednesday for some required classes. Once they found him hanging on a railing, but on the floor. He has been having most of his meals in the room. She said they're trying to get him up for meals, but most of the time they are having to feed him in his room. Now the only way they can get him to the dining room is in the chair. She said he hasn't felt good at all the last few days. I have another meeting with Amy on Tuesday of next week.

Bill seemed scared today and very clingy, wanting to be right with me wherever I went. He said part of a sentence— like, "I wish . . . ." Then he got that look in his eye, glaring at me as if to say, "I wish I knew what was going on." I asked, "Do you know where you are?" He whispered, "No." Then he whispered, "I want to go." He doesn't know where he is or where he wants to go. He is still resisting shaving, and they had to pull my picture off the wall and show him last night. They said, "Bebe said for you to get shaved." Then he let them shave him. They said they use the Bebe thing quite a bit. I said, "As long as it works, use it." He is so thin and bandaged on his arms and in different places. He bleeds so easily. When he went back to sleep, I left.

Suzanne went today, and he was very quiet and asked her what her name was. She said Suzanne Bralley. He smiled and didn't say much more. He played a little with little Ben. I got a call at 5:40 that he had fallen in the dining room. He wasn't hurt bad—just a torn bandage and bleeding again. They red-octored him and he is now okay.

When I got there, I could tell he was really irritated and cold and wet all over. I was irritated with the nurses. I stepped out in the hall and called an aide to come and clean him up. He wouldn't let her touch him, and she had to go get help. I said I would help, and Bill was really mad. He was standing up holding on to his pants so they couldn't be pulled off—mad as could be. I looked him right in the eye and said, "Bill Bralley—you turn loose of those pants. I'm changing them right now." He looked at me and said, "I hate her [the aide] and she hates me." He told the aides to get away. They were so scared and started to run. I put my hands on Bill's hands where he was clinging to his pants, and very loudly said, "Bill Bralley, I'm not putting up with this. We have to change your wet clothes. Now be nice and don't talk like that to the nice girls." He immediately let loose of the pants and leaned close to me and whispered, "I really hate her." I held his hands and she pulled the wet pants down and put a fresh clean diaper on. He was standing up and I was holding his hands. Then I said, "Sit down so we can pull them off and put the clean pants on." He was getting mad again. The aide said, "Aren't you afraid he will hit you?" I looked right at Bill and answered, "No. He won't hit me because he knows I will leave him if he does." She finally got him all dressed, but he didn't want her to button him so I did. As the aide was leaving, she said, "I wish you were here all the time." I had to laugh because all during our marriage, I always let things slide until I was pushed too far, and then I would give Bill what I called a come-to-Jesus talk. Believe me, he never failed to listen to those talks.

Later I got him up as I think it is good to keep him moving as much as possible. He was shuffling along and said, "Where's Suz?" I said, "I think she is home with her little boys." Then he said, "I mean, where is Suzanne?" But he always called her Suz. I said maybe she'd be here later. We walked quite a bit today. Later he asked again, "Where's Suz?" So I just said, "She'll be here soon." Then he said, "You know she fell?" I just barely said, "Oh." Don't know where he got that idea. He started getting dizzy, and we barely made it to the dining room. He wasn't mad anymore at anyone and sat right down in his chair. I went to "get the coffee and tea," hoping the good mood would continue and he wouldn't turn and knock poor Gilbert out of his chair, as he sometimes does. Gilbert still just loves Bill. As I left, one of the nurses told me they are giving him an extra pill tonight as his mood has been bad for two whole days.

JULY 17, 2011

I couldn't find Bill anywhere when I got there, and I got the aides looking. We looked and looked all over the west wing. Finally, I found him in a vacant room down the east wing, just sitting in a chair. He was very weak and confused. He seemed more confused than ever. I stayed while the aide went and got a wheelchair. Then I wheeled back him to the west wing and his room. I could tell he was restless. Finally he said, "I can't figure . . . ." I said, "Everything is okay." He started making the circles with his hands again and used his hands like he was pushing something away. He kept pushing something away. It reminded me of my Uncle Charlie, who used sign language.

Bill is beginning to use his hands more and more to express himself. He is pretty good at getting his idea over. He tells me to "shush" a lot. Then he signals with his hand. He'll point and show me what he wants. He can sure tell me and the others what he wants. All in sign language. He just hardly ever uses words. Everyone is understanding him pretty well. He is restless, so I got the big picture of his mother and asked him who it was. He looked and drew a circle. I said, "That's your mother." He whispered, "Mother." He started getting more irritable as the evening went on and seemed to be trying to think of something. I stayed until dinnertime.

JULY 19, 2011

I met with Amy today, and I had a good meeting with the doctor and several staffers. I could tell they were getting ready to tell me something. Finally one of them said, "It is time Bill had more care. He needs full-time care, although we are here all the time. He needs more. Round-the-clock. He is getting weaker and going downhill much more rapidly than we had expected." They said he is barely eating, although they are feeding him by spoon. He doesn't connect to entertainment or other people at all. Then again, they said, "We can't believe he still recognizes you. But you must be prepared as this cannot last much longer. His memory of you has surprised all of us. We feel that it is time to call hospice." "When?" I asked. "How long do you anticipate for Bill?" They said it is odd with Alzheimer's. It could be one month or six months. In these last stages he has to be turned over in bed more. He must have extra help, which I quickly agreed to. They want me to meet with the hospice people next week so I can make my own decisions. They do need the extra help and hospice will be paid for by Medicare. I knew this day was coming, but I had such a sadness come over me. It hit me really hard. I cried all the way home. Then I was ready to start what had to be done.

Bill was in a good mood today, and smiled a lot. He did a lot of sign language. When I asked, "How do you feel today?" he smiled and answered in sign language. The answer was that he didn't know how he was feeling. Darcy had shaved him, so he looked good and was in such an excellent mood. Maybe he is getting over the infection. The doctor said he will continue to get infections, and eventually the antibiotic will become ineffective with him.

JULY 23, 2011

Shirley, our daughter-in-law, was here, so we went to see Bill. He was in bed and had more bruised places on him. He didn't want to get up at all. He didn't feel good. We visited awhile and I could tell he was thirsty, so Shirley went and got him ice and water. He drank a lot and just wanted to go to sleep.

Shirley and I left and met Sean at the Royal Flush Yacht as they were coming in from a successful deep-sea fishing tournament. Sean had a big fish and a big smile. Then she and I went on to a nice seafood dinner.

JULY 24, 2011

I took Bill a good chocolate malt. They had just rebathed him after a bad bout of diarrhea, and had gotten him back in his room. I went straight to the room—no Bill. I hollered back at the aide, and she said, "He can't walk at all so he can't be far." Sure enough, he was in the room two doors down in another person's bed, all curled up. I'm sure glad that person wasn't there. The aide woke him up, and he was completely disoriented. I said, "Honey, you got in the wrong bed." We had to get the chair to get him back to his room. Although we thought at first that he couldn't walk, he did. He looked at me strangely, and after we got him back in bed I noticed that he kept on looking at me strangely. I said, "Bill, what are you thinking? Can you tell me?" He looked at me and said, very plainly, "I can't think." Then he closed his eyes. He never looked at anything. He just seems worn out. Finally, he dozed off. They told me they wouldn't get him up for dinner but would give him some soup when he woke up.

JULY 26, 2011

Bill was asleep and didn't seem to want to wake up. I tried hard to wake him and tried to talk to him. I'm not sure he recognized me at first, but when I leaned over to kiss him, he knew it was me and smiled. He definitely did not want to get up and move to his chair. He did a few hand signals and kept dozing off. Finally, I leaned over and said, "I've got to go. Be here later." I left because Toni was coming in from Las Vegas. (I have kept the kids posted on Bill and she wanted to be here when I met with the hospice people.) Toni looks good, and we will see Bill tomorrow.

JULY 29, 2011

Toni, Tye, Suzanne, and I all met with the hospice people at my house today. It sounds good. They will start immediately. We were informed that they will make sure he is comfortable all the time and will do everything needed to make certain of it.

Just as the hospice people were walking out, I got a call from the home. Bill had fallen again and this time had hit his head pretty hard. He was in the dining room, in his chair, and tried to get up. They said it happened quickly. The hospice rep called after she heard the call, saying they'd get someone over there right now and evaluate Bill immediately. We liked that attitude.

Toni and I went over after everyone left. He was in bed—black and blue all over. He was extremely tired, and when he looked at us, Toni said, "Daddy, it's Toni." He looked at both of us and said plainly, "Where's Suz?" We sat him up. They had washed his hair after the fall and Toni could examine his head pretty well. She said, "Yeah, there's a pretty good bump." They told me it bled quite a bit.

We laid him back down, and he just kept staring at Toni—really staring. Finally I said, "Bill, Toni is here." She leaned over really close and said, "Hi Daddy—it's Toni." Then he really smiled and said, "No way!" He grabbed her and pulled her down for a kiss. He smiled and looked so happy to see her. He just kept smiling, but we could tell he was very tired. He was dozing off. He would open his eyes, but from then on it was more of a dazed, out-of-it look. His leg must have gotten hurt. also. He must have fallen on that right leg, as he would say, "Hurts." When we said we were going to get coffee he just smiled. But he sure knew Toni. I was so glad she was there. I have a feeling she may have gotten there just in time.

JULY 30, 2011

Toni and I went to see Bill. He was in bed resting and could hardly wake up. His fingers and toes are completely white—like plastic—and he is very cold to the touch. He was extremely cold today (it's July). He had been shaved really well, and hospice had already gotten an electric bed for him with the pull-up sides. Still, they didn't get him up except to put the new bed in. I found out they had already given him pain medicine. Thank God.

JULY 31, 2011

It's Mitch and Shirley's 29th anniversary. The nurses had rolled Bill into the dining room, and he was sitting with Sam—as always. Sam was happy, and when I walked up to them, I said hi to Sam and he said, "Hi, Bebe. Hey waitress, bring drinks for everyone!" Poor Bill. He couldn't even smile when I said, "Well, Bill, we'd sure take him up for a Scotch, wouldn't we?" Bill just grimaced. I could tell he felt bad. Nurse Margaret said she had him up there just to get him up a little, but she'd appointed an aide to him so he could be watched all the time. I pushed him out in the hall by Betty's office, and he kept looking through the glass window. Then he said, "I don't know how to fix it. What are we going to do?" I talked to him, and he just sat there. He didn't feel good at all. I said I didn't feel good today either. Bill looked at me and said, "I can't fix it!" A little later he looked straight at me and said, "Tye went fishing today." I said, "Oh, it's a good day for fishing." He nodded his head as if he knew that. His life is so sad.

AUGUST 1–2, 2011

I have stayed awhile each day. He's been about the same, except he is much better shaved than ever before. He seems completely out of it—but peaceful. Suzanne had been there earlier today, and she said he had not eaten much lunch. She tried to get him to eat and tried to feed him a little, but he would turn his head. She is going tomorrow, as I am really not feeling good at all.

AUGUST 5, 2011

Bill has not been out of bed for a while now. He doesn't feel good ever. He had a skinned arm—really bad this time. It was sore. He didn't talk, but he kept pointing to something and whispered, "I can't fix it. I can't fix it." I said, "Don't worry, I can get someone to fix it." I stayed until they were bringing his tray.

AUGUST 6, 2011

Bill was on the little short couch in the front lounge—holding his head with his eyes closed. I sat down beside him. He looked at me hard and then said, "Is it really you?" I said, "Yes." He hugged me and said, "I'm glad." We just sat there a long time before getting him back in his chair. I asked if he would like to try to walk. He smiled and said, "Not really." I said, "Let's try, Bill. Don't give up." I got him pulled up, and he just held me real tight and just smiled at me and said, "No." I got the chair under him quickly. He looked up at me and said, "Bebe, I feel so bad." I asked him where he felt bad. He looked at me and circled his whole body and looked at me as if to say, "You know." His fingers are white like plastic, so cold still. There's no circulation in his feet, either. He is so thin. His skin just hangs off of him. It doesn't seem like he has any good days anymore. He just feels bad all the time. This is not living.

AUGUST 8, 2011

It's our 58th anniversary. Mitch had been traveling but came back by to see his Daddy. When we went to see Bill, he was lying down. He knew Mitch because he looked right at Mitch and said, "Mitchie." He was happy to see him, and I stepped out so Mitch could have a visit with his Daddy alone. I thought that was good. We never know what Bill will remember—bits and pieces. They had a good visit. Again, I have a feeling it may be the last. Now all the kids have gotten to have a kind of farewell visit with their Daddy.

AUGUST 12, 2011

This week has been so busy. I sold our home in 11 days. When I put it on the market, I thought it would take a year, as things are slow here. Suzanne went over to see Bill. I went later. He was sitting in the dining room all alone and didn't recognize me until I was very close to him, and then was so happy to see me. He circled his body to show he felt bad. I rolled him to his room and helped get him to bed. He just literally fell on the bed—kind of collapsed. He didn't say anything today except, "Let's go." I asked where and he looked at me as if I were supposed to make the decision but that he was ready to go.

AUGUST 13, 2011

Bill was in bed again today. They said he didn't feel like getting up, although hospice had said they were planning to get him up every day. He didn't talk at all. Just a little whisper: "Don't feel good." I stayed until dinnertime. He is so pale and looks so bad.

AUGUST 14, 2011

I went today around 1:30—just after church and getting a bite to eat. He was in a wheelchair midway down the south hall facing the wall. He didn't recognize me for a minute. I now have to be right in his face for him to see it's me. When we go down the hall, he raises his hand and waves at everyone. He doesn't even want to try to walk. I got him back to his room, and he just fell on the bed—exhausted. When I covered him, he just stared at me. He is getting to where he does that a lot. He kept staring and finally said, in a loud voice, "I want to go." Bless his heart—I don't see how he can go much further in this life.

AUGUST 16, 2011

When I got there today, they told me not to go in immediately. They were cleaning Bill. It must have been really bad. It took three of them to completely rebathe him, shampoo him, and strip all the bedding—even the plastic sheet—and to sterilize everything. When I finally got to see him, they had him sitting in his chair. He was happy to see me. He smiled and reached out for me—held my hand, and plain as day said: "I hate that guy." I just talked about something else. He wanted to lie down, but we were still waiting for bedding, so I made a little cover of the last clean comforter. He curled up and said, "I'm so tired."

I visited with the doctor earlier. He said Bill's immunity is basically gone, so I had to make the decision whether to give him more and stronger antibiotics if he gets another infection—and he will. He said, "Bebe, we can virtually keep him alive with enough medication until his heart and body give out completely. It's your decision." I said, "No more antibiotics—just comfort medication from now on." I asked him if he as an idea about how long Bill can hold on. He said, "There's just no way to tell. I will tell you that his entire body is deteriorating very fast. We now need to keep him comfortable." He will pass my opinion on to the hospice nurses so they will know my wishes. It has to be in all the records. At least I feel I am doing what Bill would want, as we have discussed this very situation many times.

AUGUST 17, 2011

The rest home called. Bill fell, but doesn't seem hurt. He's just bleeding. They bandaged him. He is okay.

Never Losing Bebe

AUGUST 19, 2011

I had a meeting with the nurse, hospice, and Lisa (the other girl that keeps records—and never smiles). Bill has lost considerable weight, but he's still able to eat by spoon when fed. They said he is not acting up and is treating everyone nicely and that they love him.

Finally, I was able to go see Bill, all wrapped up in his comforter and staring at the TV. I could tell he didn't know me today because he was so polite. Finally, I got right in his face, where he could see me well, and I said, "Do you know who I am?" He smiled and whispered, "No." I said, "That's okay. I am Bebe." He just looked at me and quietly said, "Oh."

I stayed for quite a while. He would look at me now and then. I think he wondered what the hell I was doing there. Finally I said, "We had a little rain and we sure need it for the grass." He smiled politely and looked as if he were thinking: If you want rain, lady, it's okay, but just get the hell away from me. That damn polite smile he can give—that's the one he gives when he has no idea who someone is.

AUGUST 20, 2011

I saw Bill in the hall, so I went right up to him and said, "Hi, honey!" I kissed him. He just kind of looked at me. I said, "Do you know who I am?" He whispered, "No." I said, "This is Bebe." He looked at me, and I just said, "Let's go get something to drink." He kept looking at me, and we went to a little table in the lounge. He kept staring at me. I stayed for quite a while. He seemed restless. Finally I said, "I'd better go." He still just looked at me and finally whispered, "Okay."

AUGUST 21, 2011

Bill was in his chair up next to the nurses, sitting with his eyes closed. I tapped him and hugged him. He just looked up at me. I rolled him into the lounge and tried to talk to him, but he never acknowledged me. I sat there for maybe 30 minutes and said, "Let's roll over yonder." He would just looked at me and say nothing. As I was passing the nurses' station, one of the nurses said, "Bebe, Bill's blood pressure dropped way below 100—it was dangerously low, and we think he had another ministroke today. We nearly lost him for a little bit there."

He has almost quit eating even soft food. As I rolled him to the door of the dining room, I said, "Do you want to go in there?" He looked at me and said really low, "Not particularly." I thought that was a funny answer. I took him on to his room, and as soon as he saw his bed he started trying to get out of the chair. I said, "Hold on—until I get it next to the bed. I have to help you into the bed." He was shaking so badly and was so cold. I got him in bed and covered him up really well. He closed his eyes, and he was out. He never knew me.

I went back to the nurse in charge, and she said, "Bebe, I don't know how he is holding on. It is all in God's hands." I don't think he will live until his birthday, which is October 5. He is so pitiful. He knows nothing and just stares and hurts. It used to be better when he knew me and could smile and respond a little and maybe have a happy thought now and then. I know he doesn't have a single thought now.

AUGUST 26–28, 2011

All days are pretty much the same. I go every day and he doesn't know me at all. But on Sunday, he did seem to know that I was someone who loved him because when I walked in he said, "Oh, thank God." He held out his arms and held me really tight for a long time. He didn't know (or couldn't say) anything. I'm sure he didn't know who I was, but I do think it was comforting to him for me to be there.

I just sat on the bed with him, brushed his hair a little, and asked if he had been walking. I knew he hadn't been walking at all. I asked him if he would like to try to walk. He nodded yes, so I pulled him up, but we didn't get two steps until I could tell he was going down. So I pushed the chair under him quickly and said, "Well, let's just roll over by the window."

Tye had been over early this morning and fed him breakfast. The nurse said he ate better when Tye fed him. He may have felt safe with Tye and felt like it was someone who loved and cared about him. When I had to leave I said, "I'm going." He just looked at me. I stopped when I got to the door and just looked at him. He was staring at the wall while the people around him were talking. I think words are just "blah, blah, blah" to his ears. He did some circles today and kept pointing to my T-shirt. I couldn't figure out what he was getting at.

SEPTEMBER I, 2011

I can't believe it has been almost three years since Bill has been gone from home. Now I am convinced he definitely had Alzheimer's at least two years before he came here. The movie *Trapeze* was on—a really old one. He smiled at me when I came in, but he didn't know who I was. For a minute he looked like he might know—but no. I stayed about an hour and a half and finally said, "Guess I'd better go." He just smiled and whispered, "Okay." Jason, one of the hospice nurses, called around noon and said he had been with Bill all morning and asked him some questions and that Bill answered a few. I seriously doubt that unless he just answered yes or no with his head or hands. Jason said he is eating very little. Duh? Tell me something new.

SEPTEMBER 4, 2011

Bill was sitting in his chair in the dining room just staring at nothing. He sort of recognized me. He didn't know my name or anything, but the look in his eye suggested he might have known me. At least he reached out to me when I got right up to him. He hasn't done that in a long time. I said, "Let's roll your wheelchair over there," and he said, "Okay." When we got to the door of his room, he put his feet down and wouldn't let me move him. He said, "No—not there." So I said okay, we'd go over yonder—to the lobby. He wanted to go to the window at the end of the hall, so we did. Then he said, plain as day, "I want to go." I asked, "Where do you want to go?" He said, "To our house." Very plainly, not whispering. I asked, "Do you want to go to the ranch house?" He looked at me and said, "We don't have a ranch house." I was really surprised. So I said, "Okay, we have a nice house. Do you want to go there?" He answered, "Yes, let's go." I pushed him to the lobby and we sat on the sofa. He started getting irritable, then said, "I'm ready to go." A nurse came by and said something to him, and he said, "Get away or I'll slap the hell out of you." She had been very pleasant and nice. I said, "Oh, Bill. Don't talk like that." He just looked at me. I could tell he was getting mad about something, so I just talked about other things. In a minute he leaned over and said, "You look pretty." He seemed in a better mood.

Later, when I started rolling him toward his room and we went in, I said, "Do you want to lie down?" He nodded yes, and I got him in bed. He was shaking a lot and was really cold. He doubled up and closed his eyes. He's feeling bad. He always gets irritable when he gets infections and is feeling really bad. I had thought he seemed in better health today. It is Labor Day. He talked more and had more reactions today than he has had for quite a while. I sure can't tell much.

SEPTEMBER 5, 2011

I couldn't believe it. When I got there, Bill was standing in the middle of his room—alone. I said, "Do you want to try walking?" He looked at me terrified and said, "I can't move." Apparently he didn't know where he was, what to do, or how he had gotten there. The chair was right beside him, and the bed right behind him. I don't know where all the nurses were. I helped him to the bed, and he literally flopped on it. He pointed to the peanut-butter crackers. I opened them, and he ate the whole package—plus drinking a Dr. Pepper. I think he has forgotten to look in the fridge anymore.

He was cold, exhausted, and full. He just wanted to lie down. He seemed in a good mood, seemed to know me, though not my name, but he could tell who I was. He tried to talk. He held that picture of himself and Toni dancing. I asked, "Do you know who that is?" He looked and looked. I said, "This is you and Toni dancing." He smiled and said, "Toni Baloney." Just smiled so big.

Today I did something different. He was in a good mood, so I told a little joke and he didn't catch on to it. But I laughed and laughed and then he just laughed and laughed as if he thought it was funny too. It was a sheep joke that Toni had sent me. He may have gotten it, but I don't think so. The more I laughed, the more he laughed, and that was good. He hasn't laughed in so long. He reached out for my hand and held on for dear life. Finally, he dozed off holding my hand, then I gently slipped it out and left for home.

SEPTEMBER 6, 2011

Bill had wheeled himself way down the south hall of the east wing. An aide was bringing him back to the nurses' station when I got there. He had skinned his arms up again and was all bandaged. He saw me coming this time and got really excited, so I took over the aide's job. I started rolling him and he said, "We have to get out." Plain as can be. I said, "Let's go over here." He put his feet down and wouldn't budge. Finally I said, "Where do you want to go?" He pointed and said he was cold. I moved toward his room and got him in bed. He was shaking and extremely cold. I said, "Now you can lie down." He said, "No. We have to go." Again, I said, "Okay. In just a little while."

He was getting very irritable. A nurse came in and said he had been very irritable all day. Then he looked up and loudly said, "I want to go now." We got him back in the chair and rolled him to the dining room for some lemonade. He wouldn't even touch it. Finally the old lady who knows nothing reached over and took his lemonade and drank it. He didn't notice and was looking directly at me. Again he said, "When can we go?" I replied again, "In a little while." The nurse stayed with us, just standing off to the side. He looked directly at me again and said, "You got go now." I asked, "Do you want me to go?" He answered, "Yes," then leaned over and whispered, "You gotta go while you can. I will slip out later. Get the car ready." I looked over at the nurse and said, "Well, I'm going." He whispered, "Good." He was very shaky, cold, and nervous.

I acted as if I left, and even the nurse thought I was gone. I started back around a corner to see if maybe there was something wrong that I should know about. He just kept staring off in space, and the nurse kept sitting in the same chair across the room from him. Nothing changed. He must have had some thought. I don't have any idea what it might have been.

SEPTEMBER 10, 2011

Today was funny. I walked in, glanced to the right, and Bill was all curled up on the little couch in the lounge—the type with only two cushions. I don't know how he got curled up on it—he is 6 feet tall. His wheelchair was right beside the couch. I went over and pulled up a chair and woke him up. He just looked up and smiled, then closed his eyes again and dozed off.

Eventually he woke up and wanted to go. I helped him up so we could get him in his chair, and I'll be damned if he didn't walk. Very slow, shaky, and with the shuffle. But he walked. He would not sit in the chair. An aide walked by and said he has been doing that all day—getting up and leaving the chair. He said, "We just know he is going to fall, but we can't *make* Bill do anything he doesn't want to do. It is better to just let him have his way." I had to laugh at that. I said, "You are speaking to the choir here. I know that very well. That's why I never tried to tell him what to do our whole life. That's just Bill." And that's the Bill I have always loved. Usually he is right.

Finally, we made it all the way to the dining room were three women said, loudly, "Over here! Over here! This is Bill's chair! Come here, Bill!" He didn't even seem to realize they were calling. I got him in his chair at the table, and he sat down. I went and got his ice and water. He seemed perfectly satisfied. Seems to be doing better with all the hospice help. Bill has never gone by the rules—and I don't think he will start now.

SEPTEMBER 11, 2011

Bill was sitting in the dining room in "his" chair when I got there. He seemed happy to see me. He never says my name anymore. I don't think he knows it. But he seems to recognize that I am someone he can trust and loves, because he always reaches out for my hand and pulls me down for a kiss. Then he starts whispering what he wants to do or makes circles. It is always, "Let's go—let's get outta here," or "I hurt." Today I asked, "Do you want to ride the beach?" He whispered, "No." I said, "Well, do you want to ride to the pasture?" He said, "No." I asked, "Where do you want to go?" He got really frustrated and looked as if he couldn't think—just blank. He didn't even try to answer. Finally he said, "Don't feel good." He circled his stomach.

I talked about other things, and he wanted to walk again, but couldn't. Tye had been there at noon and thought he was doing well—better than in a long time. The hospice nurse said Bill was showing a lot of improvement and doing better. Of course, my personal thoughts are, Better than what? I know they think if he can sit up an hour, that's good. They act as if he converses with them. I have watched them trying

to talk to him, and he will just nod yes or no or say, "Hurt."
When he dozes off in his chair, I guess that means good. I get
kind of disgusted with them too. They are such a damn happy
bunch. I get sick of that sometimes.

SEPTEMBER 13, 2011

Bill was totally quiet today. He seemed a little better than
the last few days, but he stayed sleepy. He didn't talk at all or
anything.

SEPTEMBER 15, 2011

Again, Bill wasn't in his room when I got there, so I
started looking. He was down at the very end of the south
hall in his chair. Just staring out the window. He seemed to
recognize me. Not my name, but he reached out and said,
"Let's go." So I pushed him toward the nurses' station. He
wanted to go down another hall. He points where he wants
to go. So we went up and down halls for a long time. Finally,
I thought maybe he could go outside. It's a pretty day, and I
asked if we could go outside. They said yes. They disarmed
his alarm, and out we went.

We were only out a little while when he wanted to go
back. I took him to the dining room, and he was mad at everything once we were inside. He stayed that way. He would cuss
and say, "Dammit. Wanna go there—dammit, go to car." He
was hateful to the nurse, and then started telling me to do
this and not that. I really couldn't understand most of it, but

I knew he thought he could get away with telling me what to do. I did the best I could, but he would slam his feet on the floor so I couldn't move his chair. Whatever I did, it made him mad. So I leaned over and said, "I'm going to get some coffee." I just walked away and told Amy that he was in a very bad mood today. "I'm tired and going home." She said he had been that way all day and they have already given him extra anxiety meds. He is just on a tear today.

SEPTEMBER 17, 2011

Late last night I got a call that Bill had fallen. His right leg and hip were hurting badly. They were taking him to the hospital. It was very late. They were taking him to Corpus Christi. I said I would meet them, and they said, "No, Bebe. Don't get out this late." I called Suzanne, and she said the same thing. "Stay home, Mom. I will go and meet the ambulance there." He was in severe pain, and they were almost sure he had broken his hip. They took x-rays and said he had a fractured hip and leg, and had badly bruised his arm and shoulder. Suzanne said he was bleeding badly. One nurse was getting ready to put the IV in, and another was going to draw blood out of the other arm for the lab. Suzanne told them, "I think you'd better wait. Do one of these at a time. He will act up if you put both needles in at once." Then another nurse came in to take his blood pressure. Though warned not to do it all at once, they did it anyway. He waylaid one nurse, hit the nurse trying to put the IV in, and really let loose. He's stronger than they thought. Suzanne said she just stood back and thought, "You should have listened to me." He had also hit his head pretty badly too, but they said it will heal. Suzanne stayed with him all night, and the next morning they sent him back to the rest home.

When I went over, he was completely out. I stayed until they got him bathed and cleaned up all the blood. They said he would sleep for several hours, and they would not be waking him up (smart). So I came home and will go back this afternoon, just to watch him and get updates. They *always* tell me, "He is doing well." They are supposed to keep him from having any pain, and they had damn well better do it.

I got back again at two this afternoon, and he was just starting to get uncomfortable. When the head nurse came in, she said that the orthopedic surgeon from the hospital had called just then and said that he had only now seen the x-rays. Bill's hip was badly fractured, and he would set up surgery and put a steel pin in Bill's leg. Then in a few weeks, Bill could start therapy. I had a fit right then and there. I said, "No way! That man is not going through surgery! He could never go through therapy if he lived through the surgery!" I called hospice immediately and came to find out that they had not been called last night when Bill fell out of bed. Anyway, the head nurse Karen was there in 15 minutes or less. I really like her. She knew I was mad. She agreed with me. She said there was no way he could live through surgery. She called our doctor, and he gave orders that Bill would have no surgery but would remain in his own room with hospice care. I am hiring extra care so he will be covered around the clock. The doctor said to double the pain medication, and we will go onto morphine when needed. Of course, Bill still has the sundowner thing.

Apparently that is what happened. We think he must have been trying to crawl out of bed over its steel railing.

Karen told me they would keep him warm and comfortable, feeding him when he feels like it. But *no* feeding tubes! I'm having him watched every minute now. I went by and told Tye, as he is leaving Monday for Florida to get a boat. The doctor said to tell everyone to do whatever they are doing or need to do. We still don't know how Bill will do, or how long it will be. But we do know that if that surgeon had done the surgery, it would have been all over for Bill and put him through a lot of pain.

SEPTEMBER 18, 2011

I went over and took my reading material. Just sat and read. He opened his eyes a few times and looked at me. Of course he did not know me. It seems like he tried to move his leg a few times. He would grimace and go back to closing his eyes. They have his leg in a splint-like thing. He really can't move it. Now they are watching closely for bed sores. It doesn't seem like he is ever in a deep sleep. Seems to be having a little more pain. The nurses came in and gave him more medication while I was there. She said she had fed him a little lunch and a little breakfast. His blood pressure was 96/73. Pulse 91. To think he used to have high blood pressure!

SEPTEMBER 20, 2011

I was prepared to spend the entire afternoon. But he was completely out of it. His mouth was drooping quite a bit on the left side. I took a photo of it. They had shaved him except for his mustache; he will not let them touch his top lip— hasn't in a long time. He's very pale and stayed wrapped up in his comforter. I left. I will see him tomorrow when the doctor is here. I will get the low-down. They had a lot of pillows under both legs today, and he looked more comfortable. His blood pressure was 101/41. I don't see how he can last much longer. Bill sure would hate living this way.

SEPTEMBER 22, 2011

I can't believe how much better he is today. He seemed rested and not so sore and in good spirits. His eye was still cloudy-looking, but he was looking toward the TV and seemed to be watching it and enjoying it. He laughed at Hoss on *Ponderosa* and when *The Jeffersons* came on, he raised his arms and kept time with the tune and even tried to sing a little of "Movin' on Up." He actually moved his shoulders, smiled, and seemed happy. I think I need a little of what they are giving him.

He didn't know me but seemed to know I was not a nurse or worker. He pointed to the big picture of his Dad and said plainly, "Do you know who that is?" I asked back, "Who?" He said, "It's Bill Bralley." That stumped me. I got the picture off the wall and held it close for him, and he said, "Yep. That's Bill

Bralley." You sure can't tell what he is thinking. And usually when he does think, it doesn't make sense.

Then he did a lot of circles with his hands as he does sometimes, and he looked at me and said, "Okay." I said, "Okay." Then he said, "I'm ready to go." I asked where, and he looked at me like that was an impossible answer. I asked, "Do you want to go to Port Aransas?" thinking it might ring a bell. He looked at me and whispered, "I guess so." Then he reached for my hand and seemed to hold on to it tighter than usual. He held it as he dozed off.

The nurse came in and said Bill is better today than he has been in a long time. He is losing more weight even though he is eating. His legs have always been big and strong, they are downright skinny. The skin just hangs off his legs. He was all shaved, except for the mustache. He needs it off, but he won't let them. They are taking extremely good care of him. So I am not going to gripe about the little things.

A Damn Good Ride

Bill was awake a little more. He smiled, and I talked to him. I said, "This is Bebe." He smiled, and I said, "Can you say Bebe?" He smiled and said, "My wife." So I knew that he knew who I was, but he never said *Bebe*. He kept holding my hand—holding tighter than ever. He had a good grip on me when he dozed off to sleep, so I had to really pull gently to slip my hand out. He doesn't seem to be in any pain. Pillows are all around him. They're keeping him clean and they called yesterday and told me he is doing so well they will have him back in the chair in two weeks. That doesn't really make sense to me, but I won't argue. I just don't want him to hurt himself again. It hurts when they change sheets and have to move him even just a little. He gets severe pain when he has to be changed.

Bill opened his eyes a little bit when I got there, reached for me, and pulled me down. I thought he had something to tell me. He kissed me and smiled. He held my hand for the longest time so tightly I couldn't get it loose if I wanted to. It was as if he were holding on for dear life. Then he started pulling on the rails of the bed as if he were trying to get up. I know he can't, but he has surprised us before with how strong he is. He kept trying, and I was telling him not to lie back down. Then the pain started, so the nurse had to come in and give pain medicine. He tried very hard to say something today. He moved his lips, but I can't understand anything. It is so frustrating for him. And me too. I don't know what, if anything, he can think of—if it makes sense, or if he does have a thought. He has tried a lot of sign language today. Then he will look as if he sees something way off that interests him. It's just the wall.

OCTOBER 5, 2011

Bill was completely out of it today. He slept most of the time I was there. It is his birthday. He is 82 years old. He seems comfortable. He opened his eyes and looked at me a little. He hasn't talked now for a while. He seemed restless and was staring a lot. No recognition of me or anything. Using his hands a lot. I think he is hallucinating because he is reaching out for things—reaching upward as if he is reaching for someone to pull him up with that one hand. Finally, he will drop his arm, as if he is tired of trying. He went back to sleep.

OCTOBER 11, 2011

Today it seemed as if he was wanting to move. He doesn't talk. He hasn't said a word in a long time. I could tell he was restless and staring a lot. No recognition of anything. He definitely sees something that no one else does. The hospice nurses agree. It's like he's in another world, and I'm not sure he isn't. It's like he isn't here anymore.

OCTOBER 19, 2011

I went early, took the Sunday paper thinking I would read while sitting with him. He was very awake. He seemed to know me. I leaned down and kissed him and said, "This is Bebe." He smiled and said, "I know." For someone who hasn't said a word in a long time, that was something. He reached for my hand and then touched my hair and smiled. I knew for sure that he knew me. His eyes told me so. I went and got the big picture of his mother off the wall and asked, "Who is this?" He looked so kindly and said, "Sweet Mother." (I actually never saw that part of her, but it just goes to show. . . Be nice to your kids when they are little because they will remember.)

He was much more alert today—more so than in the past month. He wanted to turn over or move. Of course that hurt. He kept his good eye on me the entire two hours, and he would just look at me. Then he would try to say something, and he could only get as far as opening his mouth. It seems like I could understand, "I want—." Of course, he couldn't finish. Several times he tried to say or tell me something. I would ask, "Do you want to go?" He would smile and shake his head no. Did he want water? Ice? He just kept looking straight at me. I mean, directly in my eyes—like a dog does when the dog wants something and you have to figure it out. I know it is frustrating to him, but then I think he can't remember what he wants to tell me.

Margaret came by and told me that he hadn't eaten all day today but ate a little yesterday. She walked over and put her arm around me and said, "Bebe, you know Bill is going, don't you?" I said, "I guess so, but some days he seems better." She said, "Bebe, don't be fooled by the good days. He is going fast. He may know it—and may wish you knew it." Then she said, "He is being watched all the time. You will be called in time to be with him. I promise you. Go home and get some rest, you are going to need it."

OCTOBER 20–31, 2011

The rest of October, Bill was going in and out of being awake and asleep. He has not known me or anything the rest of this month. I don't see how he is hanging on, but everyone else seems very optimistic again. I sure don't have that feeling.

NOVEMBER 1, 2011

They have raised the head of the bed higher so Bill can breathe better. I think it helps, and he can turn his head and look around a little more. I can tell he is hallucinating, as he is still reaching for something—like he is in another world and sees something or someone and stares as if he is looking at something important. He whispers to shush, as if he is listening to someone or thinks someone is listening to me.

Today he got the most frightened look I have ever seen on his face. He pulled his bedding up close around his neck, as a child does. I patted his arm and talked in a low voice about everything and told him things were going to be all right. In a minute, I felt his body relax and he closed his eyes and slept about 10 minutes. I covered him, especially his feet because they stay so cold. When he awoke, he looked at me and smiled.

He didn't know me at all today, but he seemed to feel comforted as I held his hand and patted his arm. My just being there seemed to comfort him. He kept looking at me intensely, like he was trying to figure out who I was, but he couldn't. It is so pitiful. He is just in a holding pattern, so to speak, and can't go either way right now. This is terrible for anyone to have to go through. I just keep wondering, Does he have any thoughts? What does he think? He doesn't talk at all anymore, but sometimes when he looks at me so hard, it looks like he is thinking something. He has whispered a word or two now and then, but we can't understand him because he whispers so low. He is definitely in a waiting period. I do think he knows it.

NOVEMBER 12, 2011

Shryl, one of the hospice nurses called, and we had a nice talk. At first she said, "Well, I had a nice visit with Bill today and we talked." I stopped her right there and I said, "Shryl, do you mean to tell me he talked? Or did you talk and he smiled or nodded? Please let me know—because I have someone to sit with him all the time when I'm not there or you're not there, and she has never heard a word out of him and neither have I. We have only heard whispers and see his lips move a little." Actually, I haven't had a sentence out of him in almost three months. She backed off then and said, "What I mean is that he responded to his name when I said Bill." I said, "To me that is quite different from a conversation." I did tell her how much I appreciated her and the others so much, but please don't feed me BS. That's not the way I am. Please do not tell me, "Oh, Bill is doing just fine." I am there every day, and when I miss a day, my children are there. She said, "Well, I mean, we know he is in the dying process, right? Now he is doing good for going through this process." What the hell? I guess I just don't see things the way others do. Good for dying?

I held onto my tongue and my thoughts and just asked, "Can you tell me where you think Bill is now?" She said, "Well, he has lost all muscle control. He's eating very little. The body is shutting down on its own and does not need the food. The body does that in the dying process. We are keeping him out of pain now. He is on morphine. We are turning him a little and padding him to keep the bedsores under control. It is just a matter of time. Not a long time." I said, "Thank you, I like direct information. I can't stand sugar-coating to or from anyone. I will be over tomorrow. I am just moving to another house. I knew the doctor was there today, so I don't usually go on Wednesdays as that is hair-trimming and bathing today." She was very nice and said, "I understand."

NOVEMBER 13, 2011

Bill seemed more alert today. I'll be damned if the Wisconsin people weren't right there trying to talk to him. They are really good people. After they left, he was looking at me so hard. I leaned over and kissed him, and his eyes got tears and they just streamed down his cheek. I said, "I know, we both do. It's been a damn good ride, hasn't it? I couldn't have shared it with anyone but you and . . . I will always love you." I could hardly believe it, but he held my hand and smiled a little smile. He was just looking at me every minute. He knew what I was saying, I swear.

I fed him ice. He was so hot and dry, but they said he had eaten a little and was "doing pretty good." Of course, to me that means, "Hey buddy, you are doing pretty good for dying." But I didn't say it out loud. He dozed off holding onto my hand. I don't have the nurses in when I am with him unless they have to attend to him personally or give medication.

NOVEMBER 15, 2011

Today our old movers moved me to the new little house in Portland, Texas. Not that I particularly like Portland, but right now I can't see that it matters a big damn where I am.

As they say, everyone has to be somewhere. I wanted out of the big house Bill and I shared.

I was very tired today, but thought I just had to go over. Bill is not responding to anything at all. He doesn't look at me. He's shaking terribly and reaching upward for *something*—he acts like he is trying to reach or hold on to someone's hand. He has whispered, low, "Please. Please." Several times. He looks almost dead. I mean, he looks like he is dead. I really think he is in another world now. I thought I must be the only one who thinks that. But now Suzanne does too. She was over and thinks he's dying now.

NOVEMBER 16, 2011

I came right after church and sat all day. He shook terribly. I would try to soothe him by holding his hand. He held my hand so tight I got a cramp, but never mind that. I want him to have that hand to hold onto. I know the end is very, very near. He has that death look that I've seen before. His eyes are dilated, and he has circles around them. Bill shows emotions and expressions through his eyes, but he just isn't there. He shook so badly that finally they gave him something. He closed his eyes and went to sleep.

NOVEMBER 17, 2011

They swear he ate a little food today—still hanging in there. He's gone the two previous days with no food, but they said he ate pretty well today. He's so thin and shaking so badly. He's looking upward and reaching upward. He wears out, dropping his arms as if he can't quite reach something. There's no recognition of noises or of anyone in the room. Nothing. He's breathing slowly, but I think he's really dead. I know that doesn't make sense, but I think it will be very soon when the body shuts down completely. I have a strong feeling now that Bill is gone from this world.

Suzanne went back over during Branch's football game, and she said that he was shaking badly and that he reached upwards while she was there. She saw the same things I did. She stayed quite a while. She called me to say, "Mama, Daddy is definitely dying."

NOVEMBER 18, 2011

I went over early. Bill isn't moving. There's no response to anything—not even the needles. I would have thought he was dead if I didn't see a tiny bit of breathing. I talked with the nurse who said he'd had a bad day. They've given him a lot of medication to keep him out of pain and to try to stop the shaking. I stayed all day and went home late feeling most downhearted, knowing we're near the end of our life together. I cried all the way.

At 11:30 p.m. I got a call that they had put Bill on oxygen—and that he was doing well. I said, "I'm on my way." I grabbed some clothes and got another call as I was walking out the door. "Bebe, you'd better get over here pretty quick—Bill is going. Drive carefully." It was midnight just then. He was still alive when I got there. I sat with him, holding his hand, this time very tightly in my hand. I knew the prayer I wanted to say. I knew I wanted to hold on while he passed. His breathing was so very slow. Each breath was slower than the previous one. You could actually see the color drain out of his hands. Finally, his faced turned grayish, and he breathed even more slowly. I could actually feel him slipping away. I thanked God that he was finally taking Bill out of this world to a better one, with no pain.

At ten minutes after two o'clock on the morning of November 19th, Bill drew his last breath. I stayed for a while, then stepped out in the hall and called the hospice nurse and regular nurses. I stayed with him until four that morning. It was all over for Bill. He gave it one hell of a try, bless his heart. He was ready to go. I think he was reaching for someone that was waiting for him in heaven. I believe he left this earth yesterday, and the body just took a little while to follow.

It will be a long time before someone walks in this man's boots.

Goodbye to the love of my life.

It really was fun.

Afterword

LORALU RABURN, M.D.

Dr. Loralu Raburn is the founder and owner of Clarity Endeavors, a company devoted to educating the public about brain diseases. Dr. Raburn was educated at Tulane University, the University of Hamburg in Germany, the University of Oklahoma College of Medicine, and the National Hospital, Queen Square, London, England. She is board certified in neurology and has special expertise in Alzheimer's Disease. She lectures widely on this and other topics concerning brain disorders.

Bebe's resourcefulness and deep reserves of flexibility allowed her to cope with the ever-changing behaviors that characterized Bill's dementia. In many ways she was operating in the blind, reacting to the disruptions in normal communication and activities caused by the illness.

Alzheimer's disease disrupts all the normal pathways of the brain's nerve networks, but its damage falls particularly hard on the areas serving memory. Without memory we lose our mooring to reality. Our brains connect experiences and relationships to other people throughout our lifetimes by constructing memories of events and memories of other people. Without reliable access to those memories, our internal reality becomes very different. Alzheimer's disease unleashed a cascade of network failures within Bill's brain. As his access to some memories failed, his brain substituted other memories in their place, usually older ones. Memory networks were not the only neurons affected. Bill's ability to perform complex analytical activities was also failing. He could not use the automatic reasoning skills the rest of us rely on to solve problems and make our way in the world.

Increasingly it was Bebe who shouldered these tasks. She became Bill's "peripheral brain." Bill needed her to function as a substitute thinker for him, but Bebe also needed to create and maintain a comfortable and understandable environment in which Bill could still function.

This need is brought about by the way our brains respond to a disease that targets the individual neurons, eventually destroying them. It's a battle our brains will ultimately lose. But our response to this injury is elegant: our brains have remarkable adaptability and continue to function quite well in the face of neuron damage and loss. In certain neural systems, the losses approach 85% before symptoms of dysfunction appear. This is why the onset of Alzheimer's disease is usually so very subtle. The systems are failing, but in a graceful way. The loss of a neuron here and there doesn't cause a catastrophic failure. The brain adapts and continues to function. Even the person with early Alzheimer's may be unaware of the changes. But as the disease progresses, the loss of function becomes increasingly apparent. The person's ability to maintain a stable internal reality fades as memory function degrades. Older memories are more resistant to this process than fresh ones are, and they remain accessible. Bill began to access those older memories of his earlier home address when he could no longer recall his current address. In a very real sense, he was living in the past while trying to reconcile that reality with the messages he continued to receive from his eyes and ears. Bill's reality became more constricted as the disease progressed; it is a puzzling and terrifying experience for a caregiver to observe.

Bebe certainly grasped the larger reality of Bill's day-to-day needs and activities. She took on the task of structuring Bill's constricted reality to mesh as much as possible with the bigger picture. People with Alzeimer's disease become increasingly dependent on others to shape and explain their reality to them. Since the brain's deteriorating function is discontinuous—with bursts of restored signaling as well as new losses of old patterns—Bill had good days and bad days. So Bebe faced a moving target. She entered Bill's reality and connected with him in his world while also forging a bridge to the "real world." Her drive and compassion allowed Bill to function with dignity and a remarkable degree of autonomy in the face of severe disease.

A caregiver's greatest affliction is memory. Bebe remembers Bill's integrated personality. The piecemeal loss of this person is the continuous reality she faced every day.

For Bill, his greatest *blessing* is memory. As this function decays, his overall awareness of self and others became increasingly simplified. In later stages the brain's signaling patterns run slowly and operate only on the remaining pathways not corrupted by the disease. Although there is the potential for brief periods of higher-order processing, the general order of business is to keep fundamental systems working. So basic needs such as hunger and thirst remain, if not the means to communicate them. At many levels, Bill was unaware of what was happening to him. As long as his needs were met and his environment appeared safe and stable, he could be quite content.

It helps for caregivers to realize that their loved one fails gracefully; caregivers are creating a new reality for that person to inhabit every day. Great creativity and lots of energy are needed to respond to the shifting landscape of their loved one's internal reality. The task is arduous and unrelenting. It can consume caregivers to the point of causing their own premature deaths. This memoir chronicles one caregiver's successful journey, overcoming the challenges posed by Alzheimer's disease. Bebe and Bill's experiences aren't unusual, but they are nevertheless unique. No two of us are alike and our experiences together are always one of a kind. It was their great love for one another that remained unshakable as the disease ran its course.

Bebe and all caregivers have another chapter to complete in their lives once the caregiving role ends. The pain of watching new losses appear concludes with the death of their loved one. Only then can caregivers turn to the work of self-healing: they must reintegrate into their larger roles in society, reconstruct their memories of their loved one over a lifetime of shared experiences, and restore the complex facets of their own personalities into a new individuality no longer bound by the overriding demands of being an active caregiver.

Being a caregiver is irreversible. That aspect remains within, and a part of you indefinitely. All of us know caregivers and many of us are ourselves caregivers. Caring for one another is one of our mightiest assets as human beings, and Bebe is a shining example for us all. Bebe, you make us proud.

SOME NOTES ON BRAIN FUNCTION, MEMORY, AND REALITY

The great strength of the brain resides in its interconnectivity. No single nerve cell, or neuron, is the sole keeper of information. Instead, our brains create patterns of signaling, one neuron to another. It is within the living pattern of electrical impulses that we find the language of our thoughts and actions. From the moment a neuron is formed in the developing brain, it literally begins to reach out to other neurons to form connections. The connections are both local and distant; they are so dense that a single neuron can have as many as 10,000 points of contact. A neuron's potential to signal to multiple neurons simultaneously is essentially limitless. That means our brains are capable of creating almost any network of signals between neurons. The combinations available are staggeringly complex.

After we are born, connections between neurons begin to evolve, and they continue this evolution over our lifetimes. Some connections are terminated; some are strengthened; new connections are formed. The result is a unique operating system within each brain. The basic arrangement of neurons and supporting cells is the same in all brains, but the way in which patterns of signaling develop across those structures varies enormously, especially in higher-order functions. These are activities such as problem-solving and planning for the future, decision-making and impulse control. No two brains are exactly alike.

The brain also integrates signals about our external environment, from sensory organs such as the eye, ears, and skin, with internal signals such as hunger, thirst, and a need to feel safe. Over time, neuronal networks refine these signaling patterns. Speech emerges and the brain learns to control its hardwired features such as muscle movement. Brain activity is continuous—especially during sleep. Much consolidation of waking experience takes place during slumber. Our brains create and maintain a formidable capacity to take in and process signals from the environment, analyze their significance, and formulate responses. Thus we can have a casual conversation with another person while driving down the road and enjoying a cup of coffee—and we do it without giving it a second thought. Such is the sophistication of neural programs.

Our brains also perform another function we largely take for granted. Our brains create reality.

Step back for a moment and consider the nature of reality. As physical beings, we are bound by certain unbreakable "rules" that dictate our interactions with the world outside our heads. This includes things like gravity, and the near-spherical nature of planets. But much of the rest of reality is open to interpretation. Our brains are capable of exercising imagination, and most of us have dreamed of flying (without an aircraft!). Because it's quite practical, we agree on most fundamentals of the physical world. This agreement facilitates getting along together, and it also permits us a phenomenal amount of wiggle room to interpret the world around us and the people in it.

We tend to regard reality as fixed, but upon reflection it's easy to see that a dog's experience of reality is not the same as ours. A dog's brain is heavily devoted to analysis of signals coming from the nose, while we rely more on our sense of sight. So there is Dog World reality and Human World reality. Each of us creates our own internal reality every moment, waking or sleeping. It all hinges on one facet of reality that is less concrete than water and food, yet indispensable to our comprehension of our environment. That aspect is time. If we don't perceive time passing in the same way that others around us do, we occupy a fundamentally different reality.

Anyone who has undergone general anesthesia knows that time stops as the drug takes effect, then resumes as it wears off. There is nothing between those two points, as if reality were suspended. For others, reality has continued to exist and time has continued to pass. Why? Our rational thoughts tell us that time didn't really stop and events really did take place, yet we cannot prove this obvious reality by just using internal markers. We did not form memory. It is memory that moors us to reality and gives us some basis for consensus about events that occur. If *memory* fails, *reality* fails.

How does the brain create memories? How does it store them and how does it retrieve them?

Armies of researchers have devoted decades of research to answering these questions. The short answer may not surprise you. Individual neurons in specialized brain areas are exclusively devoted to creating one-of-a-kind signaling patterns, transferring the patterns to other groups of neurons for safekeeping and maintaining a connection to those neuron groups in order to recover the pattern on demand. This is how our brains process new information, learn from it, and create a reference for the experience in holding areas of the brain. When that information is needed, the brain calls it up and sends it along to the particular brain area requesting the information.

The neurons involved in working memory are the most active cells to be found anywhere in the body. Unlike most neurons, they die and are replaced continuously. Their metabolic demands are extremely high, and like other cells they are vulnerable to slow delivery of their nutrients or any other factor that disrupts their internal chemistry. This is why memory functions go offline when these neurons are exposed to a general anesthetic, for example.

The repair and replacement activities of this special group of neurons are excellent, but not infinite. Over a lifetime, memory function becomes more inefficient. When additional stresses come into play, memory function can suffer irreversible damage.

The brain routinely forms certain toxic proteins, and when those proteins aren't eliminated efficiently, the neurons sustain progressive damage. These injuries affect the basic machinery inside the neuron and also compromise the cell wall.

Neurons live and die by the function of their walls. Electrical signals passing between neurons run along the walls, and when a breach occurs, that signal can be corrupted or cut off entirely. Repair and recovery is possible, but it takes time and energy. Energy is required not only for repair functions but also to support creation of a new route for the electrical signal to follow. This can be as straightforward as switching the pathway to a neighboring branch of the neuron (10,000 connections, remember) or as devastating as shutting down all the incoming and outgoing signals until an operational pathway can be built.

One prominent theory of Alzheimer's disease suggests that the brain forms toxic proteins that are not readily eliminated. The buildup takes years and the damage to neurons is cumulative. At a certain point the compensatory functions of the neuron fail and signaling is completely lost. This is not an all-or-nothing phenomenon. First, the signal is rerouted, slowing the transmission speed. In the larger sphere of integrated brain function, this process can be seen when we have trouble finding the right word. If the signal is temporarily lost but picked up later, a person might experience a delay in responding to a question.

When a neuron dies and the signal is permanently lost, the remaining neurons can still produce the signaling pattern—but with a "hole" in it. This is like looking at an image made up of small dots. From a distance the picture is recognizable even when some or perhaps many of the dots are missing. As the number of dots decreases, however, the image degrades to the point that it is unrecognizable. Alzheimer's disease degrades our signaling patterns in an analogous fashion.

Made in the USA
Lexington, KY
29 March 2015